Wellness
Activities
for
Youth

Volume

1

Wellness Activities for Youth

Sandy Queen

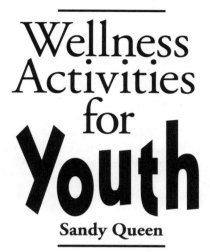

Help Youth:
- Develop a wellness lifestyle
- Prepare for life changes
- Build sound relationships
- Make wise decisions

Volume 1

WHOLE PERSON ASSOCIATES
210 W Michigan
Duluth MN 55802-1908
800-247-6789

Library of Congress Cataloging in Publication data 92-64003
ISBN 1-57025-026-X

REPRODUCTION POLICY

Unless otherwise noted, your purchase of this volume entitles you to reproduce a modest quantity of the worksheets that appear in this book for your education/training activities. For this limited worksheet reproduction no special additional permission is needed. However the following statement, in total, must appear on all copies that you reproduce.

Specific prior written permission is required from the publisher for any reproduction of a complete or adapted exercise with trainer instructions, or large-scale reproduction of worksheets, or for inclusion of material in another publication. Licensing or royalty arrangement requests for this usage must be submitted in writing and approved prior to any such use.

For further information please write for our Permissions Guidelines and Standard Permissions Form. Permission requests must be submitted at least 30 days in advance of your scheduled printing or reproduction.

Printed in the United States of America

10 9 8 7 6 5 4 3

WHOLE PERSON ASSOCIATES
210 W Michigan
Duluth MN 55802-1908
800-247-6789

Sandy Queen, Sandy is the founder and director of Lifeworks Inc, a training/counseling firm in Columbia, Maryland, that specializes in helping people take a better look at their lives through humor, laughter, and play. She has developed many innovative programs in the areas of stress-reduction, humor, children's wellness, and self-esteem.

Sandy is known as a dynamic lecturer, humorist, and educator with a special focus on the child within each of us.

Sandy speaks with inspiration and humor. Her philosophy—Lighten up! This is the only life you have!

Sandy Queen may be contacted at:

Lifeworks, Inc.
PO Box 2668
Columbia MD 21045
410-992-7665.

CONTENTS

ACKNOWLEDGMENTS

Creating a learning environment that is positive, caring, supportive, and growth-promoting, an environment in which students come to know themselves better, develop positive self-esteem, and learn about and care for others—this is the challenge of teaching wellness to kids. Some facilitators are able to create this kind of environment quite naturally, but most of us can benefit from suggestions. It is in this spirit that *Wellness Activities for Youth, Volume 1* is offered.

I am indebted to friends for some of the ideas and activities included in this book, and I am greatly indebted to the many children who have given me ideas that really work because they are student-created. All of the activities in this book have been used with real kids and have succeeded more often than they have failed. I say that because no single activity will work every time with every group. The more you get to know your students, the more you will know what activities are likely to work with them. So don't be afraid to experiment to find out what works for you and for your students.

Sandy Queen
1994

INTRODUCTION

Visit any school and you will probably find that within their mission statement is some reference to the development of the total child. Schools have always professed interest in educating the whole child, but with the current high-tech boom, falling achievement scores, and the increase in the number of students not working up to their full potential, much of the focus on the emotional and social growth of students has been set aside in favor of stepped-up academic programs. What educators need to remember is that students who like themselves—who feel competent, self-assured, and valued—perform better in the academic arena.

Wellness Activities for Youth, Volume 1 has been designed to help young people learn about themselves, examine important areas in building a wellness lifestyle, and perceive themselves in positive, self-affirming ways. Students can learn to take charge of their lives by acquiring the skills, knowledge, and strength to identify and stand up for their own values.

The activities in this book focus on growth in all major areas of wellness—physical, mental, emotional, values clarification, self-responsibility, self-esteem, relationship building, substance misuse and abuse, communication skills, and peer pressure. They can be used as a separate mini-course within your program, as part of regular lesson plans, or whenever you wish to emphasize a particular point. Although they are primarily for students from the middle elementary grades through high school, many can be adapted for use with college and adult groups as well.

Use *Wellness Activities for Youth, Volume 1* to stimulate your thinking about what you can do in your classroom or with your group to make wellness class time an enlightening and enlivening experience for you and your students.

NOTES FOR GROUP LEADERS

Wellness Activities for Youth, Volume 1 can be used by a variety of people who work with youth—counselors, camp directors, scout leaders, parents, teachers, and youth group leaders, to name just a few. Any normal, fun-loving, creative, daring, kid-loving, risk-taking facilitator can create wonderful, creative, awe-inspiring, attention-getting, fun-raising, retention-building activities! These can be built into almost any program. You don't need any special qualities, other than good judgment, a sense of humor, flexibility, and a democratic leadership style.

Before using the activities in this book, spend some time thinking creatively about your goals for your class. Then ask yourself, "How can I help my students learn what they want to learn?" When you ask this question you help create a student-centered classroom in which students become active participants in the learning process instead of passive recipients of teacher-directed material. Although having students assume a measure of responsibility for their own learning may not be feasible in all academic programs, it sets the tone for successful wellness programs.

Creating an environment in which all students can be involved in planning and implementing activities—an environment that enhances student growth through openness, cooperation, trust, and interdependence—causes classroom motivation to soar, keeps discipline problems to a minimum, and helps you and your students achieve your learning objectives.

Remember, when you raise students' *attention* level by creating an environment that is stimulating and comfortable—and fun—you also raise their *retention* level because classroom experiences that are enjoyable are remembered—along with the content!

Keep notes on what you liked about each activity and what you would change the next time. Only you know your group, and fine-tuning is important if you are to obtain the best results from your efforts.

Group discussion will stimulate students to identify, clarify, and express their feelings and concerns in an open and accepting environment. However, don't be discouraged if your first attempts at building such an environment are met with less enthusiasm than you had hoped. It takes time to build a comfort level that will encourage students to speak freely and openly.

Whenever you use any activity, first explain what is involved, especially when you are asking students to share information about themselves and their feelings. Make sure students know that there is a "pass" rule, that they will never be forced into sharing anything that is uncomfortable.

Accept students' contributions without judgment, maintain a "you can do it" attitude, listen, listen, listen, and be supportive. Always have a "no put-down" rule. When students break it, let them know immediately. Many times, put-downs are used to cover conflicting feelings. Remind students—gently—that often the person who puts another down is the one who has the real problem. That usually quiets the heckler!

Avoid using grades for these activities. If you must grade, grade on participation. If your students show up, are breathing and participating, give them A's. Grades really serve no purpose when using these exercises. Grades tend to say that one person's feelings and values are more, or less, valuable than another person's, and making value judgements about a student's attitude is exactly what we need to remove from our programming. Besides, these activities are not meant to be primarily cognitive anyway.

THE FORMAT

The format of *Wellness Activities for Youth, Volume 1* is designed for easy use. You'll find that each exercise is described completely, including: goals, group size, time frame, materials needed, step-by-step process instructions, and variations.

☞ *Special instructions for the trainer and scripts to be read to the group are typed in italics.*

✔ Questions to ask the group are preceded by a check.

➤ Directions for group activities are indicated by an arrow.

● Mini-lecture notes are preceded by a bullet.

THE CHALLENGE OF TEACHING WELLNESS

Those who direct wellness programs for adults are often trying to get participants to CHANGE—change their eating habits, change their sedentary lifestyles, change their life patterns. However, when working with kids the goal is not to change them but to help them become aware of the choices they will be facing throughout their lives, identify those values that are important to them, and learn to make good decisions based on good information.

Wellness programming for adults often contains dire warnings: if you don't stop smoking, stop eating so much fat, stop sitting around and not exercising, etc., your life may be shortened by a heart attack, stroke, or some other debilitating condition. Those warnings may strike fear into the hearts of adults, but not kids. Young people are here-and-now oriented: they don't care what will happen thirty years from now (when they are old!) as much as they care what will happen right now. They don't ask "Will it help me live longer and be healthier?" They want friends, acceptance, a chance to belong. Wellness programming for kids will be most effective if it addresses those needs.

The life-threatening consequences of some decisions—for instance, acquiring AIDS from risky sexual behavior—should be presented, but not by using scare tactics and dire statistics. Adolescents operate under a special delusional system in which the main precept is "it can't happen to me." Because they don't respond to scare tactics, use real-life examples to help youngsters realize that it CAN happen to them.

IN CONCLUSION

Wellness programming for youth is a seed-sowing adventure; the harvest won't come for many years. Your goal should be to help students become knowledgeable about themselves and their lives and to lay a foundation for lifelong wellness as early in their school years as possible. Don't expect a revolution! Overnight changes in children's behavior are not likely. It takes a long time to internalize new ideas, values, and attitudes. But, the process can be a growing experience for you and your students, and that is what is really most important. It is with great pleasure that I bring this book to you, and I hope that the time you spend with your students in these activities will be positive and growth-enhancing. I welcome comments, criticisms, and ideas about how these activities worked for your group.

Sandy Queen
1994

ENERGIZERS AND WARM UPS

1   STRING ME ALONG

After working together to create large story figures, students discuss participation and cooperation. Use this activity to explore group cohesiveness or as an integrative activity in specific subject areas.

GOALS

Promote group togetherness.

Increase sensitivity to cooperation within the group.

TIME FRAME

10–15 minutes or longer, depending on the enthusiasm of the group

AGE GROUP

Grade 3 and up

MATERIALS NEEDED

A 4-foot piece of string, ends tied together forming a loop, for each group.

PROCESS

1) Divide the class into groups of 5–6 students.

2) Give each group a string loop.

3) Advise the students that they, as a group, are to use their string loop to create the items which you will name.

4) One at a time, list the following items: circle, square, rectangle, shape of your state, fruit or vegetable, stethoscope, kite, dog, elephant, butterfly, car, person, heart, tree, flower, lungs, digestive system. Use your imagination to add to this list or to make substitutions.

5) Lead the class in a discussion of the following questions:

✔ Who led your group?

✔ Did everyone participate equally?

✔ Were there people in your group who gladly participated but didn't want to make any decisions?

✔ Were there any problems with group cooperation?

VARIATION

■ After the students complete several figures, instruct them not to talk during the rest of the activity. All their decisions must be made in silence. One at a time, list items for students to create with their string loops, then lead a discussion of the following questions:

✔ Was there a difference in leadership and participation when the activities were done in silence?

✔ Was the group held back in any way?

TRAINER'S NOTES

2   CHOOSE YOUR WELLNESS

Students broaden their understanding of wellness by choosing wellness statements that are relevant for their lives.

GOALS

Check out personal attitudes about wellness.

Expand awareness of some less obvious wellness messages.

TIME FRAME

30–45 minutes

AGE GROUP

Junior and Senior High

MATERIALS NEEDED

Wellness Sayings list; envelopes; tape.

PROCESS

1) Before class, make four copies of the **Wellness Sayings** list and cut them apart on the dashed lines. Place three copies of each saying in an envelope, and then hang the envelopes on the classroom walls. Post the fourth copy of each **Wellness Saying** above its corresponding envelope.

2) When students arrive, give the following instructions:

➤ Walk around the room, and look at all the sayings.

➤ Choose two sayings that best describe how you feel about wellness.

3) When they have completed their selections, ask the students to stand and explain, one at a time, why they chose the sayings they did and what meanings those quotes have for them.

SAMPLE WELLNESS SAYINGS

Add your own sayings to this starter list.

Wellness today is an investment in my life tomorrow.

Exercise is my primary method of stress management.

My body is a priceless possession.

I can wait until I am older to worry about wellness.

My stress is killing me!!

The only way to good health is through good choices.

I am my own best friend.

If it is to be, it is up to me.

I am what I think I am.

Friends' wishes often take priority over my own needs.

Laughter is the best medicine.

If I can dream it, I can achieve it.

I like to learn, but I don't like to be taught.

I am Good Stuff!

The most beautiful thing we can experience is ourselves.

Adolescence is a terminal illness.

Love is the most important thing in the world.

I feel in control of my life.

It's not falling down that is the problem; it is STAYING down.

Peer pressure is our biggest problem.

Injustice anywhere is a threat to justice everywhere.

©1994 Whole Person Press 210 W Michigan Duluth MN 55802   (800) 247-6789

It's not whether you get knocked down, it's whether you get up.

Winning is a habit. Unfortunately, so is losing.

Winning isn't everything, but wanting to win is.

I'll worry about all of this tomorrow.

If I could just get a good night's sleep, things would be better.

Drugs aren't the problem: PEOPLE are the problem.

I'm getting Better and Better each day.

I get so busy DOING sometimes, I forget about BEING (myself).

I'm happy to be just who I am.

I wish I was someone else.

The price of wellness is responsibility.

3   I'VE BEEN WONDERING

Students present their questions and concerns in the form of a ticket which admits them to class. The questions, which range from the sublime to the ridiculous, are great discussion starters.

GOALS

Students voice concerns and questions in a non-threatening, private way.

Students can see that many of their concerns about life are shared by others; they are not "weird" or alone in their thoughts.

Leaders can tap into what is going on in the minds of their students.

TIME FRAME

Several weeks—a few moments each day plus additional time for discussion at the completion of the activity

AGE GROUP

Junior and Senior High

MATERIALS NEEDED

Admission Tickets.

PROCESS

1) Photocopy the **Admission Tickets** worksheet and cut the tickets apart.

2) Distribute tickets to students and then give the following instructions:

➤ Each day (or week) as you come into class you must present me with a ticket in the form of a question or thought that you have.

➤ No subject is out of bounds, but be aware that at the end of this activity the questions will be presented to the class anonymously for discussion.

☞ *Over the years, I have had questions that range from the sublime to the ridiculous. Treat the funny ones with some levity; the serious ones with respect.*

3) At the end of a specified period of time—several weeks perhaps—type up all the thoughts and questions. If the same thought or question is mentioned 5 times, type the number 5 in parentheses beside it. This will let students know that this particular thought or question is on more than one person's mind.

4) Use the list of questions as discussion starters for your classes.

TRAINER'S NOTES

ADMISSION TICKETS

ADMIT ONE PERSON

I've been wondering _____

_____

_____

ADMIT ONE PERSON

I've been wondering _____

_____

_____

ADMIT ONE PERSON

I've been wondering _____

_____

_____

ADMIT ONE PERSON

I've been wondering _____

_____

_____

©1994 Whole Person Press 210 W Michigan Duluth MN 55802   (800) 247-6789

4   ADULTS ALWAYS TELL ME

This active energizer is a way for students to introduce themselves as they compare what the adults in their lives tell them about taking care of themselves.

GOALS

Get acquainted with other students.

Examine all those things we have been told by our parents about taking care of ourselves.

TIME FRAME

30–45 minutes

AGE GROUP

Elementary through Senior High (also good for adults)

MATERIALS NEEDED

None.

PROCESS

1) Ask students if they ever get tired of all the things adults are constantly telling them to do.

2) Ask them to remember some of the things they have been told by adults about taking care of themselves (i.e., "Look both ways before crossing the street." "Never talk to strangers." "Clean your plate." "Wash behind your ears.").

3) Have students take turns introducing themselves by asking them to say, "Hi, my name is_____ and I'm always being told to_____."

4) When everyone has had a turn, ask students the following questions:

   ✔ What was the funniest thing you heard?

   ✔ What was the most serious thing you heard?

   ✔ What is the thing that you heard most often?

   ✔ Were most of the things you heard pretty good rules to follow?

✔ Which ones were? Which ones were not?

✔ What do you get most tired of hearing?

☞ *As students are introducing themselves, you might want to ask, "Has anyone else been told this?" just to show that we are all told many of the same things.*

VARIATION

■ After each child has introduced him or herself, ask for volunteers to try to name as many students as they can and recall what those students were told by adults.

TRAINER'S NOTES

5   CHEER, CHEER FOR WELLNESS

Students clarify what they know about wellness as they cheer for their particular wellness topic or interest.

GOALS

Promote group cooperation and creativity.

Create cheers that will describe the various elements of wellness.

TIME FRAME

20–30 minutes

AGE GROUP

Adaptable to any grade

MATERIALS NEEDED

Wellness Topics; index cards and tape; container.

PROCESS

1) Photocopy the **Wellness Topics**, cut the copy into pieces along the dashed lines, and tape the pieces to index cards. Add additional topics that are suitable for your class. Place the index cards into a container.

2) Begin the activity by stating, "So, you've always wanted to be a cheerleader? Well, here's your opportunity!"

3) Divide the group into at least 4 groups with no more than 10 students in each group, and then give the following instructions:

   ➤ One student from your group should, without looking, select a card from this container.

   ➤ You have 10 minutes to create a cheer based on the topic on your card.

4) After 10 minutes, have each group present their cheer for the rest of the students.

5) Give lots of positive feedback and encouragement.

WELLNESS TOPICS

physical fitness	intellectual wellness
good nutrition	smoking prevention
self esteem	stress management
drug prevention	spiritual wellness
social wellness	healthy habits
environmental wellness	emotional wellness
relationships	peer pressure

©1994 Whole Person Press 210 W Michigan Duluth MN 55802   (800) 247-6789

6   GROUP GROAN

This activity breaks the classroom "quiet rule" and encourages students to share their frustrations in an enjoyable way.

GOALS

Express frustrations of daily life in a humorous, dramatic way.

Release group energy.

TIME FRAME

2 minutes

AGE GROUP

Junior and Senior High (good with adults, too)

MATERIALS NEEDED

None.

PROCESS

☞ *This activity is particularly good for perking up the group when you feel that the energy level in the room has dropped.*

1) Introduce the exercise by making the following points:

   • For all of us, some days are just the pits.

   • It seems like the whole world dumps on us.

   • It would help the energy of this class if we could just get rid of some of this frustration and negativity.

2) Continue by giving the following instructions:

   ➤ For the next minute I want you to groan out loud about all the miserable things that have happened—really let it out!

   ➤ "Ready, Set, GROAN!"

3) As students are getting into the swing of it, call out situations like:

   ➤ You have three major tests tomorrow (Groan!)

©1994 Whole Person Press 210 W Michigan Duluth MN 55802   (800) 247-6789

➤ Your mother bought you some really yucky clothes and she's making you wear them (Groan!)

➤ Your father wants to chaperone the school dance (Groan!)

4) Have students add complaints.

5) After a minute or so, say "Stop." Ask students how they are feeling and how they felt as they took some time to blow off frustration.

☞ *Sit down and continue the class session hoping that the principal does not come running down from the office wondering what has happened!*

TRAINER'S NOTES

7   JUST FOR FUN

This activity is a fun way to spend a few minutes, be creative, and review some wellness principles.

GOALS

Create a funny wellness story.

Encourage creativity and fun within the class.

TIME FRAME

10–15 minutes

AGE GROUP

Elementary and up

MATERIALS NEEDED

A copy of the **Story Lines** handout for each student.

PROCESS

1) Duplicate the **Story Lines** for each student.

2) Fold the **Story Lines** accordian style using the dashed lines as a guide.

3) Distribute **Story Lines** to the students.

4) Tell students to form a circle, and then give the following instructions:

➤ Fill in the blank on line 1.

➤ Fold the sheet so your answer does not show, and pass it to the person on your right.

➤ Complete the stories in this manner, filling in the blank of the next section, folding the paper, and then passing it on.

➤ Do not look to see what has already been written.

5) Have students read their completed compositions.

VARIATION

■ For other folded paper story writing activities, simply change the questions and use the same process. You might, for instance, write

WELLNESS IS . . . on each fold, and then ask students to write one word that best describes wellness as they see it.

When the sheets are completed, have the students share the responses with the entire class. Did most people agree and have similar answers? Were there any really 'far out' answers?

Point out that everyone has a different opinion about what wellness means and that all answers are correct because they reflect the personal opinions of the class members.

TRAINER'S NOTES

STORY LINES

Once upon a time, there was a little _____
                                          (person or animal)

who became really turned on by wellness and wanted to be REALLY
well, so he/she/it went out and bought_____ .

Then he/she/it joined _____ ,

and everyday he/she/it ate _____ ,

and did an hour of _____ .
                            (type of physical activity)

By the end of the month he/she/it had lost _____ ,

and he/she/it looked _____ ,

and felt _____ .

At the end of this experience, he/she/it said " _____
_____ ."

And he/she/it lived _____ .

©1994 Whole Person Press 210 W Michigan Duluth MN 55802   (800) 247-6789

TRAINER'S NOTES

SELF-CONCEPT

8 THE PERFECT PERSON (p 22)

Students become actively involved in creating what advertisers would have us believe is the perfect person. (45–60 minutes)

9 MAKING THE PIECES FIT (p 24)

Students create a classroom puzzle using pieces of their own individuality to complete the puzzle. This is an excellent get-acquainted activity and can be used with young children as well as adults. (20–30 minutes)

10 LOST IN A MASQUERADE (p 27)

Young people are often afraid to be who they are because of pressures from peers and society to conform to group norms. This activity lets students express creatively some of the masks they often wear to be accepted. (1–2 hours)

11 MIND GRABBER (p 31)

This change-of-pace activity demonstrates how closely the mind and body are interrelated. (10–30 minutes)

12 WHAT IS REAL? (p 34)

Students listen to the story of *The Velveteen Rabbit*, by Margerie Williams, to examine how "real" they are in their lives, what it takes to be real, and how important love is. (45–60 minutes)

13 ATTITUDE CHECK (p 36)

This activity helps young people see how others feel about some of the many issues that all people struggle with throughout their lives. (45–60 minutes)

14 TEEN SELF-ESTEEM (p 40)

In this evaluative exercise, students physically place themselves along a continuum representing self-esteem issues of teens. This is a good exercise to use at the beginning of a self-esteem program. (20–30 minutes)

8   THE PERFECT PERSON

Students become actively involved in creating what advertisers would
have us believe is the perfect person.

GOALS

Promote interaction among students.

Examine some of the distorted views of beauty and good looks that are
prevalent in today's society.

Discover that there is no one perfect person.

TIME FRAME

45–60 minutes

AGE GROUP

Junior and Senior High (great for adults, too)

MATERIALS NEEDED

A large balloon (12"-14" in diameter) for each small group; scissors; glue;
large selection of women's and fashion magazines.

> ☞ *If you have helium available, it is great fun to inflate the balloons
> with helium before beginning. This allows you to keep these
> 'perfect people' floating around your room for the day! (Use
> smaller balloons to conserve helium.)*

PROCESS

1) Begin by presenting the following questions for discussion:

   ✔ Have you ever wished that you looked like one of those perfect
   models in the magazines?

   ✔ Is there such a thing as a perfect body?

   ✔ Is there anyone on the planet that has the perfect everything—eyes,
   nose, mouth, ears?

   ✔ Wouldn't it be interesting to see what one of those perfect people
   would look like?

2) Divide the students into groups of 4–5 members; distribute balloons, scissors, glue, and magazines to each group; and give the following instructions:

➤ Blow up and tie your balloon.

➤ Look through the magazines and find the perfect eyes, nose, mouth, ears, and hair, and create the face of this perfect person.

  ☞ *Some will also add bodies; this can add some real creativity to the activity!*

3) After all the groups have completed their perfect person, gather the class and give the following instructions:

➤ One group at a time, stand and present your perfect person to the rest of the students.

➤ Explain why you chose the particular characteristics that you did.

➤ Describe the overall effect of all the perfect parts.

➤ Keep your presentations brief.

4) Lead a discussion, making the following points:

• There is no such thing as a perfect person.

• If you take all the perfect parts and put them together, you come up with a gross distortion of a person.

TRAINER'S NOTES

9   MAKING THE PIECES FIT

Students create a classroom puzzle using pieces of their own individuality to complete the puzzle. This is an excellent get-acquainted activity and can be used with young children as well as adults.

GOAL

Create a puzzle made up of pieces represented by each person in the group.

Help students appreciate the individual uniqueness of each person and the beauty of the whole group.

Help group members get acquainted and learn about each other.

TIME FRAME

20–30 minutes

AGE GROUP

Middle Elementary to adults

MATERIALS NEEDED

Heavy paper, large enough to cut 9" x 9" puzzle pieces for each student; magazines; markers; glue; crayons; scissors.

PROCESS

1) On a large piece of heavy paper draw a puzzle with interlocking pieces. Enlarge the **Puzzle Pattern** or adapt it. Make sure that there is a piece for each student.

   ☞ *Before cutting out your puzzle, write numbers on each of the pieces and directional arrows to aid you in reconstruction. This will help you make speedy work of putting the puzzle back together. Write the numbers large enough and dark enough so that students will know not to use that side to decorate. (Someone always completes the wrong side, even in adult groups—no, ESPECIALLY in adult groups!)*

2) Cut out the pieces and distribute one to each student, along with magazines, markers, glue, crayons, and scissors.

3) Give the following instructions:

   ➤ Use words, phrases, and pictures to create a small collage about who you are.

   ➤ Work on the blank side of the paper.

   ➤ Be creative and fill up the entire puzzle piece.

4) After the students complete their pieces, and are busy with something else, reconstruct the puzzle, tape the pieces in place, and display it on the wall.

5) Use the assembled puzzle to point out how the individuality of the class members went together to create this wonderful work.

6) Leave the puzzle displayed in the classroom for several days.

VARIATION

■ As they create their pieces of the puzzle, have the class focus on the specific aspect of wellness that you want to study—sexuality, intelligence, friendship, family relationships, etc.

TRAINER'S NOTES

PUZZLE PATTERN

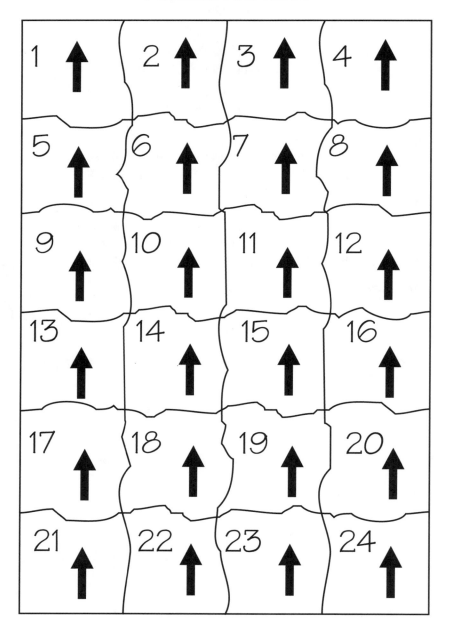

10 LOST IN A MASQUERADE

Young people are often afraid to be who they are because of pressures from peers and society to conform to group norms. This activity lets students express creatively some of the masks they often wear to be accepted.

GOALS

Examine the masks we often wear to belong to the group.

Get a better idea of who your SELF really is.

TIME FRAME

1–2 hours

AGE GROUP

Junior and Senior High

MATERIALS NEEDED

One **Mask Outline** for each student; magazines; scissors; glue; markers.

PROCESS

1) Enlarge the **Mask Outline** pattern and make a copy for each student.

2) Introduce the activity by leading a discussion based on the following questions:

   ✔ How difficult is it to be yourself around your family, your friends, and other people?

   ✔ With whom is it most difficult to be yourself? Why do you think this is true?

   ✔ Do you really know who your "Self" is?

   ✔ What or who influences how you see yourself at any given time?

   ✔ How much impact do friends have on how you see yourself? What is the impact of your family, advertising, school, and society?

   ✔ What are the masks we often wear to hide who we really are?

   ✔ How do you feel when you are wearing one of these masks? Real? Phony? Scared? Confident?

✔ If you were to continue to wear a mask, and you were never allowed to really be yourself, what do you think would happen to you over time?

3) Make the following points about hiding behind masks:

- We all wear masks at some time during our lives. We all, at some time, try to be what others would like us to be so that we can be accepted or liked, or get a job, or win favor with someone. That's part of human nature. The problem comes when masks become the norm and we lose ourselves in the process of trying to please others.

- It is often difficult for teens to get out from behind the masks because there are so many shoulds that friends and society give you. You should be good looking; you should wear all the right clothes; you should be seen with all the right people; you should do drugs, drink alcohol, smoke cigarettes, have sex. Sometimes it is difficult to know who you really are. The peer group has such a tremendous influence on the lives of most teenagers, it is sometimes difficult to know that there really is a Self living inside of you.

4) Ask the following questions about peer pressure:

✔ Have you ever not gotten good grades on purpose because the group said it wasn't cool to be smart?

✔ Have you ever gone against your personal values about smoking, drinking, or drugs because the group made you feel unaccepted if you didn't participate?

✔ Have you ever directly violated a family rule because of group pressure?

✔ Have you ever used language that made you feel uncomfortable just because the group used it?

✔ Have you ever pretended to be something you are not because it made you more acceptable to the group?

5) Make the following comments:

- Being yourself is a hard thing to be when you aren't really sure who your Self is. And when the masks that you wear cover the person you really are, your true Self doesn't have the space to grow and be.

- Recognizing the masks we wear is one way to make sure that they do not gain control of us.

- All of us wear masks at some time. That is part of finding out what fits for each one of us. The important thing is that the mask doesn't block the growth of the Self and hide the real person.

6) Distribute a **Mask Outline** to each student, or have them draw their own. Instruct them to cut out the mask.

7) Distribute magazines, scissors, glue, and markers.

8) Instruct students to decorate their masks with pictures, words, phrases, and slogans taken from magazines or made up by themselves—to depict the kinds of masks they have found themselves wearing to impress or be part of the group.

9) When the students are finished, use their masks as discussion material, and then put the masks on a bulletin board under the heading "Masks We Wear."

VARIATION

■ Have students decorate one side of the mask using slogans, phrases, or pictures to depict the way they think others see them—or the way they look and act to be part of the group, and have them decorate the other side to show who they really are—the Self they often keep hidden. This may be a difficult assignment for some students so be very sensitive and don't push for any more self-disclosure than students are willing to give.

☞ *This is a good activity to use with groups outside of the classroom, at youth conferences, for instance, where it is more acceptable to be one's Self than it would be in a school setting.*

TRAINER'S NOTES

MASK OUTLINE

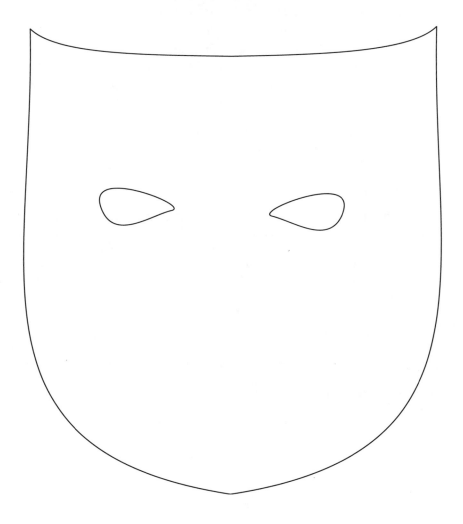

11 MIND GRABBER

This change-of-pace activity demonstrates how closely the mind and body are interrelated.

GOALS

Explore the mind-body connection.

Demonstrate the power of thoughts and attitudes over the energy and strength of the body.

Help students see what kind of power we give away when we let others control our attitudes.

TIME FRAME

10–30 minutes

AGE GROUP

Middle Elementary and up

MATERIALS NEEDED

None.

PROCESS

1) Ask a volunteer to stand next to you with both arms outstretched, one hand resting on top of the other. Tell the student that you are going to push down on his hands and you want him to resist you with all of his strength.

2) Gently push down on his hands and notice how strong he is when he is resisting you.

3) Now tell him to repeat after you: "I'm dumb. I can't do anything right. I'll never get it right. No matter how hard I try, I'll never be any good," and other negative statements.

4) Ask him to extend his arms again and have him try to resist you. He won't be able to. Even with gentle pressure, you will be able to push his arms down.

5) Discuss how negative talk has taken away his strength.

©1994 Whole Person Press 210 W Michigan Duluth MN 55802   (800) 247-6789

6) Repeat the process, only this time have him repeat the following: "I can't do it—yet. But I'm going to do it. I may not be perfect, but I'm going to be the best I can be. I don't even have to get Straight A's; I only have to be the best I can be, because I am Good Stuff!"

7) Ask him to stretch out his arms again. This time you should be able to lean on his arms without them giving way. Discuss how positive self-talk helps us feel better about ourselves and strengthens us.

8) Have the student extend his arms for a test to make sure he is strong. Now say all the negative things to him that you did in the beginning, but have him counter each negative statement with a positive one, such as "I like myself" or "I am Good Stuff." Push down on his arms. He should be strong.

> ☞ *In every group there will be some students who say that the negative images made them stronger. Rather than argue, suggest that it may have been difficult for them to concentrate.*

9) Discuss the following questions:

   ✔ What does this experience tell us about the ways in which our feelings, attitudes, and words affect our health and strength?

   ✔ How can we protect ourselves from other people's negativity? We need to go around each day with a quiet positive attitude that we truly ARE Good Stuff and that we CAN do it and that we ARE great! This will help ward off the negativity that other people may shoot at us during the day and will help us be strong enough to make good decisions about our lives and health.

VARIATION

■ For an enjoyable variation, you be the volunteer.

1) Ask a student to test your strength while you resist her.

2) Then have her say things to you like "You're really dumb. You're the dumbest teacher in the school. No one really likes you." (It may take some encouragement to get her going, but once she gets going, watch out! Kids love having this opportunity to tell the teacher off.)

3) Have her push down on your arms. (You will probably be weaker from having heard all of those negative things from her.)

4) Then extend your arms again and have her push down. You probably have lost much of your strength. Discuss that even though you knew she was just kidding, your subconscious mind BELIEVED all those negative things, and sapped you of your strength.

5) Tell her to change the words: "You are the world's greatest teacher. Everyone really likes you. You are the best in the world."

6) Extend your arms again and have her push down. You have suddenly gotten stronger.

TRAINER'S NOTES

12 WHAT IS REAL?

Students listen to the story of *The Velveteen Rabbit*, by Margerie Williams, to examine how "real" they are in their lives, what it takes to be real, and how important love is.

GOALS

Help students examine what being real in our lives is all about.

Note the people in our lives who help us feel most real.

Discuss how realness changes over the life of the individual.

Help teens understand that adolescence is a time when realness begins, but doesn't end for many years.

TIME FRAME

45–60 minutes

AGE GROUP

Junior and Senior High

MATERIALS NEEDED

None.

PROCESS

1) Read *The Velveteen Rabbit* to the class.

2) When you finish, begin a discussion by asking the following questions:

   ✔ When do you feel most real?

   ✔ What is real?

   ✔ Are teens capable of being really real?

   ✔ When does real begin? End?

   ✔ Do you care about being real?

   ✔ What kinds of people contribute to our wearing of masks and staying unreal?

✔ Can love change us? How? When? What kind of love?

✔ Is being real painless?

✔ What can we do about the pain of becoming real?

✔ What are some of the issues we need to face in our journey to realness?

TRAINER'S NOTES

13 ATTITUDE CHECK

This activity helps young people see how others feel about some of the
many issues that all people struggle with throughout their lives.

GOALS

Investigate feelings and attitudes about life issues.

Compare results and get a sense of the variety of feelings within the group.

TIME FRAME

45–60 minutes

AGE GROUP

Junior and Senior High

MATERIALS NEEDED

Blackboard and copies of the **Attitude Scale** worksheet for each student.

PROCESS

1) Distribute an **Attitude Scale** worksheet to each student.

2) Give the following instructions:

> ➤ Do not write your name on your paper.

> ➤ Answer honestly. There are no right or wrong feelings or answers.

> ➤ You will have about 15 minutes to complete the **Attitude Scale**.

3) When students are finished, collect the papers and redistribute them
throughout the class.

4) Tally the answers on the blackboard, then have the students discuss the
following questions:

> ✔ Look at the **Attitude Scale** you have in front of you. Why do you
think the person who completed it answered the way he or she did?

> ✔ Now look at the tally on the blackboard. Do most people feel the
same about the same issues, or is there a variance in the feelings?

> ✔ How can our feelings about an issue affect the way we behave in that
situation?

©1994 Whole Person Press 210 W Michigan Duluth MN 55802   (800) 247-6789

VARIATION

■ When the students are filling out their worksheets, ask them to write down their sex—but not their names. When you tally the answers, record the males' and females' in separate columns. Include the following questions in the discussion:

✔ Are there any differences between genders in the answers?

✔ Is it usual for there to be differences between the attitudes of girls and boys? Why or why not?

✔ Who is likely to be more influenced by peers—girls or guys?

TRAINER'S NOTES

ATTITUDE SCALE

Circle the letters beside each item to indicate whether you agree strongly, agree slightly, are neutral (don't care one way or the other), disagree slightly, or disagree strongly.

Please answer honestly. There are no right or wrong answers or right or wrong feelings. Your feelings belong to you and they are okay! **Do not sign this paper.**

AS   Agree Strongly
as   agree slightly
N   Neutral (don't care one way or the other)
ds   disagree slightly
DS   Disagree Strongly

AS   as   N   ds   DS   1. If you can't do something well, there's no point in doing it at all.

AS   as   N   ds   DS   2. If someone criticizes you, that means he or she doesn't like you.

AS   as   N   ds   DS   3. To be happy, I must have the approval of my friends.

AS   as   N   ds   DS   4. How I feel about myself depends on how others feel about me.

AS   as   N   ds   DS   5. If a person I care for does not care for me, that means that I am unlovable.

AS   as   N   ds   DS   6. Without friends, I am a nobody.

AS   as   N   ds   DS   7. Unless I have someone special in my life, I can't be happy.

AS   as   N   ds   DS   8. Being liked is more important than being respected.

AS   as   N   ds   DS   9. If I get a failing grade, that means that I am a failure.

AS as N ds DS 10. If someone gets a better grade than I do, that means he is a better person.

AS as N ds DS 11. If my friends want me to do something, then I should do it if I want them to be my friends.

AS as N ds DS 12. People who are good looking are happier than people who aren't.

AS as N ds DS 13. If someone I care about is angry with me, it destroys my day.

AS as N ds DS 14. Money is more important than anything to be successful in this world.

AS as N ds DS 15. My moods are caused by my friends and what happens to me. I really have little control over them.

AS as N ds DS 16. I must be there for anyone any time they need me.

AS as N ds DS 17. I have the responsibility to keep those close to me happy.

AS as N ds DS 18. If I do something nice for someone, they will do something nice for me.

AS as N ds DS 19. If something bad happens, I have a right to be upset.

AS as N ds DS 20. My friends' needs are more important than my needs.

AS as N ds DS 21. The more popular someone is, the happier he or she is.

AS as N ds DS 22. I would give up my best friend to have the girlfriend/boyfriend that I want.

14 TEEN SELF-ESTEEM

In this evaluative exercise, students physically place themselves along a continuum representing self-esteem issues of teens. This is a good exercise to use at the beginning of a self-esteem program.

GOALS

Examine what affects self-esteem in teens.

Examine personal and group attitudes about teen self-esteem.

Promote group interaction and discussion.

TIME FRAME

20–30 minutes

AGE GROUP

Junior and Senior High

MATERIALS NEEDED

Chalk or masking tape.

PROCESS

1) Prior to beginning this activity, find a 20-foot-long clear area of wall or floor space.

2) Using chalk or masking tape, make a large X at the beginning and end of the 20-foot space and at the 5-, 10-, and 15-foot points.

3) Ask students to consider the following questions:

   ✔ On a scale of 1 to 5, with 1 being Great and 5 being Miserable, what do you think the current level of self-esteem is in most teens?

   ✔ What factors influence the increase or decrease in self-esteem among teens?

4) Point out to the students the 5 X's on the wall or floor, telling them that the first X represents great self-esteem, and the last X represents miserable self-esteem. The line that connects them becomes the self-esteem continuum.

5) Give students the following instructions:

> ➤ On a piece of paper jot down where you believe most teens are in their level of self-esteem—great, miserable, or somewhere in between.

> ➤ Stand along the line of X's at the place you indicated on your paper.

> ➤ Please think for yourself. Don't just line up where your friends are or where you think you are expected to be.

6) Ask students to share with the group why they chose the place that they did, and then ask the following questions:

> ✔ What things keep teens from placing higher on the continuum—toward Great?

> ✔ What things keep teens from sliding toward Miserable?

7) Ask students to return to their desks and to write about their own self-esteem, noting where they would put themselves on the continuum.

VARIATIONS

■ If there is sufficient trust level in the class, have students physically place themselves on the point on the continuum that represents their own self-esteem. If they are in a different place than their first position, ask why this is.

■ Ask students to evaluate how other people affect their self-esteem. Have students place themselves on the continuum based on how the following people affect their self-esteem. Call out one at a time parents, teachers, friends, ministers, coaches, counselors, relatives, youth group leaders, heros, politicians, employers.

Discuss reasons why and how these people contribute to the self-esteem level of teens. Note that there may be some contradiction in the way students view some people. Discuss these differences. Is there any one category of people that make an overall positive or negative contribution to their self-esteem?

> ☞ *The "parent" category should give you lots of good discussion material, as some teens see their parents as a negative influence, while others see their parents in a positive role.*

TRAINER'S NOTES

PERSONAL WELLNESS

15 WELLNESS SHIELD (p 44)

Students will visualize their wellness lifestyles through words, pictures, and slogans by creating a wellness shield. (1–2 class sessions)

16 TAKING CARE OF MYSELF (p 47)

This activity helps students identify the things they do each day that contribute to their well-being. It helps them see that even the small things they do can add up to positive benefits for themselves. (15–20 minutes)

17 WHAT DID I DO FOR MYSELF? (p 49)

This journaling activity helps students evaluate positive daily activities that can move them up the wellness continuum toward high level wellness. (1 or more weeks)

18 I AM JOE'S BODY (p 53)

This lively activity helps students identify the functions of various body parts and the risk factors associated with not taking care of the body. (45–60 minutes)

19 MY FAVORITE FOODS (p 55)

Students use a worksheet and discussion to analyze the nutritional quality of their favorite foods and to explore their food preferences. (45–60 minutes)

20 MEDICINE MAN (p 59)

Students examine empty medication containers to understand the uses of health care products and their precautions. (45–60 minutes)

15 WELLNESS SHIELD

Students will visualize their wellness lifestyles through words, pictures, and slogans by creating a wellness shield.

GOALS

Visualize wellness from an individual's point of view.

Celebrate the things students do in their lives that they feel proud of.

Analyze and identify students' strongest and weakest wellness areas.

Encourage students to set goals for areas of wellness that may need work.

TIME FRAME

1–2 class sessions

AGE GROUP

Upper Elementary through Senior High

MATERIALS NEEDED

A **Wellness Shield** outline for each student; magazines; markers; glue; and scissors.

PROCESS

1) Enlarge and photocopy a **Wellness Shield** for each student.

2) Announce that students will be creating a wellness shield that will depict the areas of wellness where they do the best, as well as help them set goals for an area in which they may not be as strong.

3) Distribute the **Wellness Shields**.

4) List the major areas of wellness on the blackboard: physical, emotional, intellectual, nutritional, stress, spiritual, environmental, etc.

5) Give students the following instructions:

➤ From the list on the blackboard, choose the four areas of wellness in which you feel most accomplished, and write one of them in each quadrant of your **Wellness Shield.**

➤ Decorate your shields using words, pictures, drawings, or slogans (ones that you make up or that you take from the magazines or both) that will illustrate and describe how you see yourself in your top four wellness areas.

6) After students have completed work on the front of their **Wellness Shields**, continue the activity with these instructions:

➤ Turn your shield over, and divide it in half horizontally.

➤ Choose one area of wellness in which you feel you need some work.

➤ Use words and pictures to describe and illustrate on the top half of the shield what a positive lifestyle would look like in that area.

➤ On the bottom half, write 3 or 4 goals that will help you achieve a higher level of wellness in this area.

7) Using the following questions, discuss with the students how positive wellness lifestyles help shield us in our lives.

✔ Can your shield help another person?

✔ If we all put our shields together, what would happen to our classroom? The school? Our families? The world?

✔ Were any wellness areas left out, or under-represented? Why do you think this is? What could be done about this?

✔ Is there any area that you did not include on your shield as one of your top four areas, but would like to work on?

8) Have students share their creations with the class, and use the completed shields as a classroom display.

9) Use the shields as the basis for classroom skits based on the good things students see in their own personal wellness lifestyles.

VARIATION

■ For younger children, enlarge the shield pattern to create a life-sized shield that will give them lots of room to decorate with their wellness illustrations. When the students complete their shields, tape a loop of rope on the back of each shield so that the shield can be held.

©1994 Whole Person Press 210 W Michigan Duluth MN 55802   (800) 247-6789

WELLNESS SHIELD

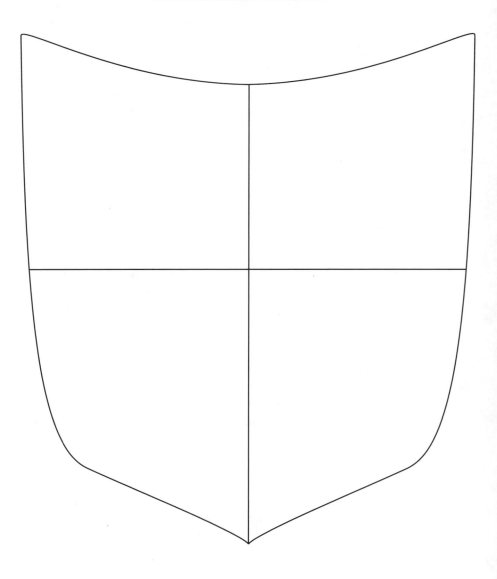

16   TAKING CARE OF MYSELF

This activity helps students identify the things they do each day that contribute to their well-being. It helps them see that even the small things they do can add up to positive benefits for themselves.

GOALS

Become aware of personal wellness patterns.

Lead students to appreciate themselves for the positive things they do for themselves each day.

Identify self-care and self-responsibility as major factors in personal wellness.

TIME FRAME

15–20 minutes

AGE GROUP

Adaptable to all

MATERIALS NEEDED

Blackboard or newsprint; paper and pencils.

PROCESS

1) Begin by asking students to list the things they do each day that they may take for granted, but which contribute to their health and well-being. Write the list on the blackboard.

   ☞ *Add the following items if students do not mention them: brushing teeth, combing hair, bathing, walking, exercising, drinking water, eating, studying, sleeping, laughing, controlling stress, saying "no" to drugs.*

2) Make the following points:

   • These are the things that, added up over a lifetime, create a large part of our health and well-being.

   • The more of these positive behaviors we begin as young people, the more healthy we are likely to be as we get older.

3) Form groups of 4 or 5 members and have the groups brainstorm all the good things they do for themselves during the day, making a list to be shared with the whole class.

> ☞ *To encourage participation, make this a contest. The group that has the longest list wins.*

4) Upon completion, have the groups read their lists to the entire class.

5) Make a master list on the board.

6) When the list is completed, use the following questions for discussion:

✔ Who is responsible for your having these habits? Who taught you?

✔ Who is responsible for your carrying these out on a daily basis?

✔ Which are the easiest to remember?

✔ Which are the most difficult?

✔ Which ones do you forget to do the most?

✔ Which ones do you never forget to do?

✔ Which ones do you think you will continue to do as you grow older? Which ones do you think will change as you grow older?

✔ Are there any behaviors listed here that you don't do, but that you think you would like to have as part of your daily life?

✔ How can you get started?

✔ Why is it important to have these kinds of habits and behaviors in our lives?

7) As you conclude the activity, compliment the students on their wonderful self-care habits and encourage them to keep it up!

VARIATION

■ If you are working with a small group of children you can have each student make her own personal list of all the things she does for herself throughout the day that are health-enhancing.

17 WHAT DID I DO FOR MYSELF?

This journaling activity helps students evaluate positive daily activities that can move them up the wellness continuum toward high level wellness.

GOALS

Analyze wellness behaviors in various dimensions of wellness.

Evaluate personal wellness behaviors.

Encourage students to continue setting personal wellness goals.

TIME FRAME

1 or more weeks

AGE GROUP

Junior and Senior High

MATERIALS NEEDED

One copy of the **Taking Care of Myself** worksheet for each student each day of the activity.

PROCESS

1) Photocopy the **Taking Care of Myself** worksheet. Each student needs a worksheet for each day of the activity.

2) Introduce the activity with a chalktalk, making the following points:

   • People who are concerned about personal wellness want to be well-balanced. They strive to take care of themselves in all areas of wellness and don't just concentrate on one or two areas.

   • Sometimes we aren't even aware of some of the things we do to keep ourselves in balance—or what we do to get out of balance.

   • To help us see how well we are doing in balancing our lives, we are going to journal the positive things we do for ourselves each day in the various areas of wellness—physical, emotional, stress management, social, spiritual, and intellectual.

©1994 Whole Person Press 210 W Michigan Duluth MN 55802   (800) 247-6789

3) Distribute the worksheets, then give the following instructions:

> ➤ Use one worksheet for each day. At the end of each day, think about the things you did for yourself during the day that contributed to your well-being. Don't focus on the negatives—only the positives. This activity isn't about what's wrong with us; it's about what we are doing well! It helps you appreciate all the positive things you do for yourself.

> ➤ Under each wellness heading, list the things you did for yourself that day. For example:

Physical: walked to school instead of riding the bus; went to track practice; took the stairs instead of the elevator; played frisbee with the dog; remembered to eat breakfast; ate an apple this afternoon instead of a candy bar.

Emotional: confronted Jim about my book he had lost—explained to him why I was angry; went to the pep rally and cheered for the team; laughed at a joke my little sister told me; cried because Jennifer hurt my feelings.

Spiritual: watched the sun rise this morning—felt really peaceful; listened to some soothing music this evening to unwind from the day; went to the church youth group meeting; prayed before bed; read some inspirational poetry.

4) Have students journal for a week. Encourage them to write in their journals each evening.

5) Midway through the week, divide the class into groups of 4–5 students and have them discuss their findings about their personal wellness balance. Being in small groups enables students to encourage each other and to share ways of dealing with areas that are overloaded or with ones that are neglected.

6) At the end of the week, have students gather in their small groups again to review their progress.

7) Ask the groups to discuss the following questions:

> ✔ Which were your strongest areas?

> ✔ Which area did you find most difficult to balance? Why?

> ✔ Could you be overlooking ways to bring balance to this area? For example, many students find that their spiritual area is neglected because they relate spiritual balance mainly with church attendance. Are there other things you can do to attain spiritual balance?

8) Decide with the students whether or not to continue journaling for an additional week. This decision will depend on how the class has taken to the project and what benefits you see arising from the experience.

TRAINER'S NOTES

©1994 Whole Person Press 210 W Michigan Duluth MN 55802   (800) 247-6789

TAKING CARE OF MYSELF

PHYSICAL

EMOTIONAL

STRESS MANAGEMENT

SOCIAL

SPIRITUAL

INTELLECTUAL

18 I AM JOE'S BODY

This lively activity helps students identify the functions of various body parts and the risk factors associated with not taking care of the body.

GOALS

Review the structure and functions of the body as it relates to a wellness lifestyle.

TIME FRAME

45–60 minutes

AGE GROUP

Middle Elementary and Junior High

MATERIALS NEEDED

Two pieces of white bulletin board paper; masking tape.

☞ *Prior to using this activity, obtain an overhead transparency or slide showing the inside of the human body. Project the image onto a student to ensure that the projected image is life-sized. Then, from the same distance, project the image onto the pieces of white bulletin board paper. On one piece, trace the outline of the body image; on the other piece, trace the outline of each of the body parts. Color the body parts, cut them out, mount the parts separately on cardboard, and, if possible, laminate for preservation.*

Suggested body parts: Brain, heart, lungs, stomach, kidneys, large and small intestines, liver, and pancreas—major bones and reproductive organs are optional.

PROCESS

1) Tape the body outline to a bulletin board. Just for fun, name your body "Joe."

2) Divide the class into groups of five students. Randomly distribute the cardboard body parts to each group, or number each part and have a student from each group choose a number and receive the corresponding body part.

©1994 Whole Person Press 210 W Michigan Duluth MN 55802   (800) 247-6789

3) Give the following instructions to the small groups, allowing time for discussion between instructions:

➤ Identify your body part and brainstorm the function or functions this particular part plays in the body.

➤ Brainstorm and record ways in which "Joe" can take care of this particular organ.

➤ Decide upon and record any risk factors associated with Joe not taking care of this particular body part.

➤ Select someone from your group to wear the organ in its correct location on his or her body, attaching it by loops of masking tape.

➤ Report your findings about this body part to the rest of the class. The other students can fill in any missing pieces of information regarding the function, care and risk factors for that particular organ.

4) Collect the cardboard body parts and place them in their appropriate locations on the body outline.

VARIATION

■ Make puzzles from drawings of various parts and systems of the body. Give each group a puzzle. Have groups put the puzzles together and then identify and describe the functions of the organs or systems.

TRAINER'S NOTES

19 MY FAVORITE FOODS

Students use a worksheet and discussion to analyze the nutritional quality of their favorite foods and to explore their food preferences.

GOALS

Evaluate personal food favorites for nutritional quality.

Observe how family habits and cultural standards may affect decisions about foods.

TIME FRAME

45–60 minutes

AGE GROUP

Elementary to High School

MATERIALS NEEDED

One copy of the **My Favorite Foods** worksheet for each student; calorie/nutrient value charts—available through the Food and Nutrition Council or in many mass-market paperbacks.

PROCESS

1) Distribute the **My Favorite Foods** worksheet.
2) Give the following instructions for filling out the worksheet. Pause after each step so that students have enough time to complete each instruction:

   ➤ List your ten favorite foods, starting with your most favorite.

   ➤ In column A, place a checkmark next to the foods you would not want to give up even for a week.

   ➤ In column B, place a checkmark next to the foods that were your favorites even when you were a little kid.

   ➤ In column C, place a checkmark next to the foods you have eaten in the last week.

   ➤ In column D, place a checkmark next to the foods you think will still be on your list when you are 35 years old.

➤ In column E, place a checkmark next to the foods you think are nutritious.

➤ In column F, place a checkmark next to the foods you listed that probably would be disliked by many other people.

➤ In column G, place a checkmark next to foods that are part of your national heritage.

➤ At the end of your list, add any foods that are served in your home on special holidays that you think may be different than those served in the homes of most other people.

3) Divide the class into groups of 4–5 students.

4) Ask students to compare their lists with members of their group and to discuss differences in food preferences.

5) After a few minutes, lead a discussion by posing the following questions:

✔ Is there a food on your list that didn't appear on anyone else's list?

✔ How many foods on the lists were culturally determined?

✔ Are there any generalities that you can draw about the nutritional preferences of young people?

✔ How do you think your nutritional choices will change over the years?

6) At the bottom of their **My Favorite Foods** worksheets, have students rank the qualities that affect their choices in foods. Number 1 is the most important, 5 the least important.

7) Have students look at the foods checked in column A and ask them the following questions:

✔ Do your favorite foods reflect the qualities in foods that you just ranked as most important?

✔ Do you select food on the basis of taste or nutrition?

8) Distribute lists of calories and nutrients. Instruct students to analyze their top two favorite foods for calorie, fat, and nutrient values.

9) After the students have completed this analysis, lead a discussion by asking the following questions:

✔ Were there any surprises about your favorite foods?

✔ Were your favorites low in calories?

✔ Were your favorites low in fat?

✔ Were your favorites low in vitamins and minerals?

✔ If you continue to eat these foods regularly throughout your life, what will happen to you? Will you have good nutrition? Will you have any trouble controlling your weight? Will your fat levels be low or high?

10) Have students share with the group what they found out about their favorite foods.

11) You may want to compute a class average on calories or fat for the favorite foods of most students.

TRAINER'S NOTES

MY FAVORITE FOODS

I. Beginning with your most favorite foods, rank the ten foods you like best.

	A	B	C	D	E	F	G
1.							
2.							
3.							
4.							
5.							
6.							
7.							
8.							
9.							
10.							

II. Holiday and special-event foods.

III. Rank the qualities of your favorite foods in order of importance. Write a 1 by the most important quality; 5 by the least.

Nutrient content _____

Number of calories _____

Cost _____

Taste _____

Friend's favorite _____

20 MEDICINE MAN

Students examine empty medication containers to understand the uses of health care products and their precautions.

GOALS

Illustrate the number of medicines that we keep in our homes.

Provide an enjoyable way of displaying and studying medication packaging.

TIME FRAME

45–60 minutes

AGE GROUP

Middle Elementary and up

MATERIALS NEEDED

Bulletin board paper; empty packages of health care products.

> ☞ *Complete Step 1 in the class period before the one in which you'll be using this activity.*

PROCESS

1) Instruct students to ask their parents for package containers (no actual medications) of products in their homes that are used for health care. Encourage students to bring in as many different types of product containers as possible—including, for example, pain medications, sleep preparations, cosmetics, digestive medications, ointments, salves, cough medicines, cold remedies, prescription drug bottles, sinus medications, antiseptics, and medications for eye, ear, nose, and throat problems.

2) Trace the outline of a student on bulletin board paper. Label the outline "Medicine Man."

3) Have students tape their product packages to the area of the Medicine Man outline for which this medication was intended.

4) Discuss the following questions:

✔ What conclusions can we draw about the number and types of medications that we all have in our homes?

✔ Are these considered drugs? Why?

✔ What precautions should be used in handling these substances?

✔ What do we need to know before we use any of these products?

✔ Where can we get the information we need to make an informed judgment about these products?

✔ What is the difference between a prescription drug and an over-the-counter drug?

✔ Are over-the-counter drugs safer than prescription drugs?

VARIATION

■ Assign students to count the number and type of medications contained in their medicine cabinets at home. EMPHASIZE THAT THEY NEED THE HELP OF PARENTS IN THIS ACTIVITY. Use the following questions for discussion:

✔ How many prescription drugs are in your medicine cabinet?

✔ How many over-the-counter preparations are in your cabinet?

✔ Where do you keep most of your medicines?

   ☞ *The bathroom medicine cabinet is the worst place for medicines due to the moisture and humidity in the bathroom.*

✔ Is your cabinet locked and out of reach of younger brothers and sisters?

✔ What rules do you have in your home about taking medicines?

✔ What is the last medicine you took? What was it for?

   ☞ *Make sure you send a note home with younger students that explains to their parents what the goal of this activity is and also the importance of their assistance with this project.*

STRESS AND COPING

21 A QUIET VIEW OF STRESS (p 62)

This activity helps students see how remembering or visualizing something pleasant can help alleviate stressful feelings. (25–30 minutes)

22 ALL STRESSED OUT (p 65)

This activity helps students to identify major stressors and to realize that stress comes from what we think about situations, not from a situation itself. (30–40 minutes)

23 COPING WITH TELEVISION (p 69)

In this activity, students look at the good and not-so-good ways that television characters cope with life. (At least two class periods plus out-of-class assignment time)

21 A QUIET VIEW OF STRESS

This activity helps students see how remembering or visualizing something pleasant can help alleviate stressful feelings.

GOALS

To use slides to help students visualize something that can bring them peace.

To help students become aware how changing their thought patterns can change their stress levels.

To examine physiological responses to stress.

TIME FRAME

25–30 minutes

AGE GROUP

Upper Elementary to Senior High (good for adults, also)

MATERIALS NEEDED

Nature slides with NO people pictured in them—use 10–12 slides for younger students, more for older; Biodots; soft music. (Choose music that is soothing. Many New Age pieces, such as Steven Halpern's *Zodiac Suite,* work well with this activity.)

Slides are available through Lifeworks, P.O. Box 2668, Columbia, Maryland 21045. 10 slides/$12; 25 slides/$30; 50 slides/$45 (prices include shipping)

Biodots are available from Biodot International, P.O. Box 2446, Indianapolis, Indiana 46206.

PROCESS

1) Begin with a chalktalk about stress:

- When we are under stress, our hands may become cold and clammy and our faces warm and flushed.

- To relax, we must reverse that process; we must warm up the hands and cool down the face.

- Sometimes, just getting away from a stressful situation for a while can help us relax.

2) Ask the students, "Have you ever felt peace and calm from watching the sun set, or clouds float by, or waves roll up an ocean beach?"

3) Tell students that you are going to show them some slides of nature. Make sure you have a variety of slides picturing different sights (i.e., lakes, rivers, oceans, forests, mountains, sunsets, clouds).

4) Tell students that you want them to view the slides without talking. If they see a scene that reminds them of a place they have been or of something they have seen—a place that brought them calm and serenity—they should close their eyes and put themselves into that scene, remembering how it felt to be calm and peaceful.

5) Distribute Biodots.

☞ *Biodots are temperature-sensitive adhesive dots that measure hand temperature by changing colors. The calmer a person is, the bluer the dot; the more stressed, the darker—brown to black—the dot becomes. Dots should be placed on the fleshy area near the thumb on the back of the hand. Biodots will not work accurately in temperatures that are too cold or too warm.*

6) Give the following explanatory information:

- When you are tense, your hands will be cold and clammy and your dot will be brown or black. As you relax, the dots will change colors from black to tan to green to blue to purple—really relaxed!

- Notice what color your dot is now. Some people are more relaxed in certain situations than other people would be. Look around at the people around you and notice the various colors of the dots.

- Note that we are all sitting here in the same room, experiencing the same environment, and yet some of us are tense, and some are very relaxed.

☞ *You may want to ask a student whose dot is blue to help you demonstrate what can happen when a person is put under stress. Have the student stand in the front of the room and ask him or her to describe some embarrassing situation, such as a first kiss. Usually, this causes the color of the dot to change quickly from blue to brown.*

- The purpose of this activity is to try and find a "calming place" in the slides—a place where you can take yourself for a few moments and experience feelings of peace, warmth, and calm.

- Your state of relaxation will be evidenced by a change in the color of the dots.

7) Lower the lights in the room. Start the music and show the slides.

8) When finished, remain quiet for a few moments with the lights off. Then turn the lights on and have students observe what if any change occurred in their dots.

9) Present the following questions to help students understand the process:

   ✔ What can we learn from this experience?

   ✔ In times of tension, do you think you can remember this quiet place— the clouds, the beach, the sunset—and take yourself there in your mind for a small escape from the negative effects of stress?

   ✔ If your dot did not change color, why do you think that happened?

VARIATION

■ If Biodots are not available, have students watch the slides and explain how the pictures made them feel, and how they could help themselves feel that way again. Ask them to recall a particular slide that brought back memories and emotions from a related experience.

TRAINER'S NOTES

22 ALL STRESSED OUT

This activity helps students to identify major stressors and to realize that stress comes from what we think about situations, not from a situation itself.

GOALS

Identify major life stressors.

Rank stressors to analyze their impact on our lives.

Recognize that everyone has different "stress triggers."

Understand that we are responsible and able to control our reactions when stressed.

TIME FRAME

30–40 minutes

AGE GROUP

Middle Elementary to High School

MATERIALS NEEDED

Blackboard; a sheet of notebook paper for each student.

PROCESS

1) Have yourself and the students list on the blackboard twelve highly stressful situations that have happened to you or them. The list may include examples similar to the following: having a huge argument, taking a big test, sneaking out of the house, failing a test, going to class without having done the homework, riding a roller coaster, getting a driver's license, dealing with peer pressure, kissing someone for the first time.

2) Give the following instructions:

➤ Tear a piece of notebook paper into twelve pieces.

➤ Copy the twelve items from the blackboard to your pieces of paper, one item per piece.

> ➤ Rank the events in the order of their stressfulness to you. The most stressful event will be on the top, the least stressful event at the bottom.

3) When students have completed their rankings, tabulate the results, write them on the blackboard, and ask the following questions about each item on the list:

✔ Why might this event be stressful?

✔ What kinds of differences are there in the way that class members feel about this stressor?

4) Say the following: "Everyone responds to stressful situations in different ways. One event may cause you a great deal of stress, but may not bother me at all. That is because it is not the event that causes us our stress, but what we think about that event that bothers us."

5) Select one student who reacted very strongly to an event or circumstance and another who reacted only slightly to the same situation. Ask them why the same event caused the two of them to react in such different ways. Ask them what they were thinking during the event.

6) Illustrate this principle by copying the following chart on to the blackboard.

	Event	Thought	Reaction
Person A	Roller coaster ride	I'm going to die!	Terrified
Person B	Roller coaster ride	This is great!	Exhilaration

7) Say the following: "It wasn't the roller coaster ride that caused person A to be terrified; it was her thoughts about what might happen to her that caused her reaction.

8) Tell students to look at the ranked list on the blackboard. Ask them to consider what they were thinking to cause a particular event to be stressful for them and, if comfortable, to share this information with the class.

9) To help students become aware of how their thoughts, rather than actual events, create stress, encourage them to remember when they were little kids and were sure that monsters lived under their beds. Ask the following questions:

✔ How did you react?

✔ Were there monsters? Of course not, but that didn't stop your fear. Your thoughts convinced you that you were in grave danger of being devoured every time you walked by your bed.

✔ What finally convinced you that there were no monsters?

✔ Does walking by your bed at night cause you any stress now? Probably not, because you are past the point of thinking there are monsters hiding under your bed.

✔ What are your monsters now? Friends? Peer pressure? Parents? School? Work? Grades?

✔ Are these monsters causing your stress or are your thoughts about them causing your stress?

✔ How can we change our thoughts to help us change our stress levels?

10) Give the following instructions:

➤ Look again at the way you ranked the stressors.

➤ On a separate piece of paper, write their primary fearful thought about your top three stressors.

➤ Now write a change-of-thought statement that may help you reduce the stress surrounding this event or situation.

For example:

Roller coaster stress thought: I'm going to die.
Change of thought: This will last only one minute. I don't have to ride this roller coaster ever again.

Peer pressure stress thought: They're not going to accept me.
Change of thought: I'm OK just the way I am. If they don't accept me, that's their problem.

Adolescence stress thought: I'll never grow up and get out of here. I'll be a kid forever.
Change of thought: In five years, I'll look back on this and laugh. This, too, shall pass.

11) Explain that there are three kinds of thinking that go on in stressful situations.

• **Irrational thinking**—includes catastrophic thinking (What if . . . I'll just die) and absolutistic thinking (I must . . . I need to . . . I have to . . . I should).

• **Rationalization**—involves an attempt to slough off the importance of the event (so what . . . who cares . . . doesn't bother me . . . big deal).

©1994 Whole Person Press 210 W Michigan Duluth MN 55802   (800) 247-6789

- **Rational thinking**—involves making preferences based on rational thought (I would like to . . . it would be good if . . . I prefer).

- Irrational thinking results in greater worry because the person imagines what is going to happen.

- Rationalization results in procrastination because the person denies the importance of the situation. This also interferes with decision making and increases avoidance behavior.

- Rational thinking means that you are using your thinking and decision-making skills in a calm way to maximize your chances of reducing stress and making good decisions.

12) Have students look at their lists of fearful thoughts and ask them the following questions:

✔ What kind of thinking was evident in your stresses?

✔ How much were your thoughts responsible for your reaction to an event?

✔ How can we control our thoughts in stressful situations so that we don't handle the situation negatively?

TRAINER'S NOTES

Thanks to Jenny Trotter of the Wholistic Stress Institute in Atlanta, Georgia, for the ideas that led to this activity.

23 COPING WITH TELEVISION

In this activity, students look at the good and not-so-good ways that television characters cope with life.

GOALS

Analyze how coping skills are integrated into television programs.

Analyze how these skills fit into our personal lives.

Recognize the impact of the media on our own coping skills.

TIME FRAME

At least two class periods plus out-of-class assignment time

AGE GROUP

Upper Elementary to Senior High

MATERIALS NEEDED

One **Coping with Television** worksheet for each student.

PROCESS

1) Introduce this activity by telling students that they will be watching television programs and examining how the TV characters cope with stress.

2) Ask the class to list the television programs they want to watch and to analyze.

3) Divide the class into groups of 4–5 students, and assign one program to each group.

4) Distribute the **Coping with Television** worksheets and ask students to complete them as they watch the television programs.

5) At the next class meeting after the students have viewed their programs, ask them to meet in their small groups and consider the following questions:

   ✔ What kind of program did you watch—adventure, mystery, drama, comedy?

   ✔ What were the major kind of stressors you saw in your programs?

✔ What was the major coping technique used by the characters—fighting, drinking, smoking, vandalism, violence?

✔ What similarities can you see between the characters and your own life?

✔ Do you use any or all of the same coping techniques?

6) Gather the class then list on the blackboard the stressors and coping techniques observed by the students. Determine the three most common stressors and the three most common coping techniques used by characters in the television programs.

TRAINER'S NOTES

COPING WITH TELEVISION

Watching television gives us many ideas about how people cope with life. Use this form to evaluate the program to which you have been assigned to watch. Bring this form back to class for discussion.

What type of program was this? Situation comedy? News? Sports? Cartoon? Mystery? Other?

What kinds of stressors were apparent during this program segment?

What kinds of coping skills were used by the characters during this program? Eating? Drinking? Alcohol? Smoking? Exercise? Talking? Drugs? Withdrawal? Aggression? Violence? Vandalism? Other?

Did any of the characters use good coping skills?

Did any character insist on using negative coping skills?

How well did the coping skills work in the lives of the characters?

Do you think this program was realistic in the way it showed people handling stress? Why or why not?

TRAINER'S NOTES

©1994 Whole Person Press 210 W Michigan Duluth MN 55802   (800) 247-6789

SOCIAL WELLNESS

24 SPEAK UP (p 74)

This enjoyable activity helps students realize that much of our daily conversation is carried on nonverbally. (20–30 minutes)

25 I THINK YOU'RE SWELL (p 78)

This activity promotes cohesion among class members and enhances self-esteem. (40–50 minutes)

26 THIS IS HOW I FEEL TODAY (p 80)

In this ongoing project, students select words and phrases that reflect their feelings about themselves and add them to a collage. (A few minutes each day)

27 YOU DID SOMETHING NICE (p 82)

To turn the tables on tattling and to make it OK to say nice things about others, try this activity. (One or more weeks)

28 QUALITY FRIENDSHIPS (p 83)

This brief activity encourages students to determine the qualities they most respect in a friend and for them to look for those qualities in themselves. (25–30 minutes)

29 FRIENDS ARE IMPORTANT (p 86)

This activity helps students look at friendship and consider what they are willing to do to be accepted. (45–60 minutes)

30 WISH FOR WORLD WELLNESS (p 89)

This activity helps students change their focus from their own personal wellness to a more global perspective. (20–30 minutes)

31 LOVE, AMERICAN STYLE (p 91)

This activity helps males and females observe the differences in their respective ideas about what love and sex are all about. (1–2 class periods)

24　SPEAK UP

This enjoyable activity helps students realize that much of our daily conversation is carried on nonverbally.

GOALS

Examine nonverbal methods as a powerful way of communication.

Emphasize that good communication is more than just verbal.

Build awareness of the many nonverbal signals used in conversation.

TIME FRAME

20–30 minutes

AGE GROUP

Elementary to Senior High

MATERIALS NEEDED

Copies of the **Body Language Words** handout; several 3" x 5" cards for each student; tape.

PROCESS

1) Photocopy the **Body Language Words** handout. Cut the phrases apart on the dashed lines and tape one phrase on each 3" x 5" card. Prepare several cards for each student.

2) Introduce the activity by making the following points:

- Even though we talk a lot every day, over 90% of our conversation is nonverbal—that is, it is done without using any words.

- We use our bodies, hand gestures, and facial expressions to communicate much of how we really feel. As a matter of fact, your body language almost always tells the real truth about how you feel, even when your words say otherwise!

- For example, when was the last time you saw a friend walk in, shoulders hunched over, and a downcast look on her face? What did you say to her? Probably, "What's wrong?" In response, she may have said, "Nothing . . . nothing is wrong. Really." Now, what did you believe, her body language or her words?

- Experts tell us that we have over 7,000 different body language words that are communicated by how we look and how we carry our bodies.

3) Distribute several **Body Language Words** to each student and then give the following instructions:

  ➤ One at a time, stand, and without speaking, convey the words or phrase given to you, using only your bodies, facial expressions, and hand gestures.

  ➤ Watch closely as each student acts out a word and try to guess what the word is.

  ➤ Think of other body language "words" that say the same thing.

4) When the students have finished acting out their words, challenge them to pay attention to those around them for the rest of the day or for a week and to report back to the class what they have observed about the relationship between body language and verbal language.

5) Use the following questions for discussion:

  ✔ How does understanding body language help you be a better communicator?

  ✔ How does understanding body language help you be a better listener?

  ✔ How does understanding body language help you understand people better?

TRAINER'S NOTES

BODY LANGUAGE WORDS

BODY LANGUAGE WORDS

Why?	I feel happy.
No!	I feel scared.
OK!	I feel depressed.
Please.	I am angry.
Please come here.	I am tired.
Please stop!	I am bored.
Listen to me, young man!	Don't hit me.
Listen!	The light is too bright.
Look!	It's dark in here.
Wow!	Go away.
I don't feel well.	I wonder . . .
I feel sad.	I feel guilty.

I don't know the answer.	Hmmm . . .
Come on, let's go!	You can't go in there.
What time is it?	I'm lost.
There's too much noise!	I'm frustrated.
I've lost something.	Where are you?
I'm feeling impatient.	What did I do?
I'm really nervous.	Get out of my way.
Be quiet please.	Kiss me.
Oh, no!	Give me a hug.
I really like you.	I can't figure this out.
I can't stand you.	I can't hear you.
I didn't do it.	Speak up.
Oh, yeah?	Follow me.

©1994 Whole Person Press 210 W Michigan Duluth MN 55802   (800) 247-6789

25 I THINK YOU'RE SWELL

This activity promotes cohesion among class members and enhances self-esteem.

GOALS

Offer students an opportunity to concentrate on the good things about someone else in the class.

Give students a chance to have nice things said about them.

TIME FRAME

40–50 minutes

AGE GROUP

Middle Elementary to Senior High

MATERIALS NEEDED

A good supply of magazines, particularly women's magazines with lots of advertisements; scissors; glue; large pieces of paper; slips of paper with students' names written on them; box.

PROCESS

1) Place slips of paper with students' names in a box, and then give the following instructions:

   ➤ Draw a name but do not reveal whose name you've picked.

   ➤ Complete a collage about this person using positive jingles or advertisements from magazines.

   ➤ Remember that you must use only positive words and pictures.

   ➤ Even though you may not particularly like the person whose name you chose, you can find things about that person that are special.

2) When the collages are completed, have the students share their collages and have the rest of the class try and guess the name of the person described.

©1994 Whole Person Press 210 W Michigan Duluth MN 55802   (800) 247-6789

3) Ask students to comment on the collage that was made for them. The following questions can help elicit discussion:

✔ Did this person get the "real you" on paper?

✔ Did this portrayal please you?

4) Display the collages on a bulletin board, and then later give the collages to each student as a memento.

☞ *It is important that this remain a positive experience. Tolerate no negative comments.*

VARIATIONS

■ Have students choose one word or phrase from a magazine that best describes who they are, and create one classroom collage from the phrases selected by all the students. Have students tell why they chose that particular phrase, word or jingle to describe themselves.

■ Younger children will find it easier to create a collage about themselves. You may want to personalize this activity by using an overhead projector to cast the shadow of each child onto a large piece of paper. Trace the shadows, and then have the students fill in their silhouettes with words and pictures. Cut out the silhouettes and display them around the room.

TRAINER'S NOTES

26 THIS IS HOW I FEEL TODAY

In this ongoing project, students select words and phrases that reflect their feelings about themselves and add them to a collage. If students are setting wellness goals, they can add words that describe how they are doing on their wellness journeys.

GOALS

Encourage students to think about how they feel and to find words and pictures that describe those feelings.

Give permission for students to express negative feelings.

Illustrate day to day changes in feelings.

TIME FRAME

Several weeks—a few minutes each day

AGE GROUP

Middle Elementary to Senior High

MATERIALS NEEDED

A good supply of magazines, particularly women's magazines with lots of advertisements; scissors; glue; one 6" x 24" strip of paper for each student; bulletin board.

PROCESS

1) Advise students that they are beginning an extended project that will help them think about changes in their feelings.

2) Distribute the strips of paper, scissors, glue, and magazines, and give the following instructions:

   ➤ Choose one word or phrase from a magazine that best describes who you are.

   ➤ Glue it at the top of your strip of paper.

   ➤ Post your collage on the bulletin board.

©1994 Whole Person Press 210 W Michigan Duluth MN 55802   (800) 247-6789

3) On a regular basis, provide time for students to add words and phrases
to their collage. Make the following points:

- If you feel rundown, upset, or angry on a particular day, include
phrases that describe those feelings.

- It is important that you tune into how you are really feeling and not
just include words that make it sound like you are always on top of
the world.

4) Have students periodically evaluate their collage by responding to the
following questions:

✔ Are there more positive than negative words on your collage?

✔ Is there any one theme that runs throughout your collage?

VARIATION

■ Instead of selecting magazine pictures, phrases, and words, you may
want to have the students write on their paper the one word that best
describes how they are feeling each day. Periodically evaluate the ratio
of positive and negative feelings on the collages.

TRAINER'S NOTES

27 YOU DID SOMETHING NICE

To turn the tables on tattling and to make it OK to say nice things about others, try this activity.

GOALS

Encourage students to see the good in others.

Create an atmosphere for validating each other.

TIME FRAME

One or more weeks

AGE GROUP

Elementary

MATERIALS NEEDED

A large decorated box, captioned "I Saw You Do Something Nice"; sheets of paper and pencils placed next to the box.

PROCESS

1) Introduce this activity by giving the following instructions:

   ➤ Watch carefully all week long and try to catch at least two people each day being helpful or kind.

   ➤ Write that kind person's name on a piece of paper along with what you observed, (i.e., Mary helped Jim find his library book).

   ➤ Place the piece of paper in the "I Saw You Do Something Nice" box.

2) Check the box and add your own observations. See that each child is mentioned at least once.

3) At the end of the week, read aloud the contents of the box. Give the sheets to the children to take home, or make a wall display.

4) Continue the activity for several weeks, or until children tire of it.

28 QUALITY FRIENDSHIPS

This brief activity encourages students to determine the qualities they most respect in a friend and for them to look for those qualities in themselves.

GOALS

Rank the qualities that students see as important to friendship.

Compare one's self to this list of qualities.

TIME FRAME

25–30 minutes

AGE GROUP

Junior and Senior High

MATERIALS NEEDED

Blackboard; copies of the **Qualities of a Friend** worksheet.

PROCESS

1) Distribute the **Qualities of a Friend** worksheet to each student and give the following instructions:

➤ Cut the worksheet into pieces along the dotted lines.

➤ The words printed on the pieces of paper are qualities that you might want to find in a friend. Look at the pieces of paper and decide which qualities you believe are most important.

➤ Sort your pieces of paper arranging them from the most important qualities of a friend to the least important.

2) After 3 minutes, tally the results on the blackboard.

3) Use the following questions to initiate a discussion:

✔ What quality or qualities are the most important to our class?

✔ Why do you think that these qualities ranked as high as they did?

✔ Why do you think that the lower ranking qualities are not as important to the members of our class?

©1994 Whole Person Press 210 W Michigan Duluth MN 55802   (800) 247-6789

4) Ask students to resort the pieces of paper to show how they see
themselves as friends, and then ask students what differences they
found between themselves and the ideal friend.

☞ *If there is sufficient trust in the class, you can tally these results
as well. The most important thing, however, is for students to
compare what they think is most important in a friend to how they
see themselves.*

5) Have students rank the pieces of paper a third time to show how they
think others see them as friends. Ask the following questions:

✔ Why do you think that others would rank your qualities in this way?

✔ How do you compare to your ideal friend?

✔ How might you become a better friend?

☞ *The little pieces of paper add a different element so that this is not
just another pencil and paper activity.*

TRAINER'S NOTES

QUALITIES OF A FRIEND

Athletic	Good listener
Popular	Brave
Good looking	Trustworthy
Smart	Creative
Wealthy	Has exciting stuff to do
Kind	Life of the party
Truthful	Can handle adults
Sense of humor	Respectful
Religious	Cheerful

©1994 Whole Person Press 210 W Michigan Duluth MN 55802   (800) 247-6789

29 FRIENDS ARE IMPORTANT

This activity helps students look at friendship and consider what they are willing to do to be accepted.

GOALS

Examine the value of friendship in our lives.

Explore the relationship between personal values and the importance of having friends.

TIME FRAME

45–60 minutes

AGE GROUP

Upper Elementary to Junior High

MATERIALS NEEDED

Blackboard; copies of the **Belonging** worksheet.

☞ *This activity should be preceded by a discussion about the importance of friends, how the need to have friends affects our lives, and the things we do to belong.*

PROCESS

1) Introduce this activity by making the following points:

- Peer pressure is a persistent issue with young people because you may constantly feel "on stage."

- You may believe that you are constantly being watched and evaluated by your peers.

- This can sometimes create situations in which you must decide whether having a friend is more important than sticking by your personal values, and whether belonging to the group is the most important thing in your life.

- The issue of belonging is a source of many problems for young people.

- In this activity you will be asked to consider what you are willing to do to have a friend and to belong to the group.

2) Distribute the **Belonging** worksheets to each student and have them spend a few minutes completing their worksheets.

3) Select one of the following three methods for tallying the worksheet answers depending on the level of trust in the classroom: Either ask students to report their answers, and then complete a classroom tally of results; or redistribute the worksheets randomly throughout the class, then tally and discuss the results; or collect the worksheets and tabulate the results for discussion during the next class period.

4) Discuss each item on the worksheet, asking students to relate situations in which they or their friends had to make this or a similar decision.

5) Continue the discussion with the following questions:

✔ Why are friends so important?

✔ How does friendship change from elementary school to junior high (or junior high to senior high)?

✔ How do you choose friends differently now than you did when you were a little kid?

✔ What difficulties do you encounter in trying to make and keep friends?

✔ Why is it that some kids never seem to have any friends?

✔ What is the most important quality of a friend?

TRAINER'S NOTES

BELONGING

If I wanted to belong to a group or wanted to have someone as my friend, I would be willing to . . .

Yes   No   Maybe

____   ____   ____   Give up the friends I have now.

____   ____   ____   Do something I think is wrong.

____   ____   ____   Break the law.

____   ____   ____   Try drugs.

____   ____   ____   Drink alcohol.

____   ____   ____   Do something on a dare that may be dangerous.

____   ____   ____   Do something that would interfere with school work.

____   ____   ____   Stop getting good grades if my friends think good grades aren't important.

____   ____   ____   Disobey my parents in order to make points with my friends.

____   ____   ____   Do something my parents wouldn't like.

____   ____   ____   Lie.

        (800) 247-6789

30 WISH FOR WORLD WELLNESS

Part of being a well person is reaching out to others and sharing the message that we all have the choice to make our lives and our world better. This activity helps students change their focus from their own personal wellness to a more global perspective.

GOALS

Create a list of wellness possibilities for our world.

Examine a more global focus for wellness.

Consider what wellness would be like in the future if we all got "on board."

TIME FRAME

20–30 minutes

AGE GROUP

Upper Elementary to Senior High

MATERIALS NEEDED

Blackboard; newspapers and newsmagazines.

PROCESS

1) Distribute newspapers and magazines, and ask students to scan them for articles dealing with international problems.

2) Ask students to identify some of the world's problems that relate to wellness, reminding them to consider more than just physical wellness. List these problems on the blackboard.

3) Ask students to list four wishes for the world that could be accomplished if the whole world decided that wellness was a good idea.

4) Prior to the next class, write the student's wishes on strips of paper. Create a bulletin board by arranging the strips around a large colorful globe.

5) Use the following questions for discussion:

✔ Which area of wellness (physical, social, emotional, relationship, spiritual, stress management, etc.) relates to each wish?

✔ Which area of wellness held the majority of wishes?

✔ How many duplicate wishes were there?

✔ In which element of wellness does the concept of peace reside?

✔ What was the most common wish for wellness among the class members?

✔ What was the most unusual wish?

6) Discuss ways your class could make a positive difference in making one of these wishes come true, and then, as an ongoing class project, take steps toward making one of these wishes happen.

7) In the middle of the globe on the bulletin board, make a list of what the students are doing that will help make their wish come true.

8) At the end of the project, discuss the activities of the group and their feelings about what they have or have not been able to accomplish.

TRAINER'S NOTES

31 LOVE, AMERICAN STYLE

This activity helps males and females observe the differences in their respective ideas about what love and sex are all about.

GOALS

Help students gain insight into what it means to be male and female in today's society.

Identify differences between the male and female points of view concerning sexuality and love.

TIME FRAME

1–2 class periods

AGE GROUP

Junior and Senior High

MATERIALS NEEDED

Magazines; scissors; tape; glue; a large sheet of paper for each small group.

PROCESS

1) Divide the class into groups of 4–5 students, with each group consisting only of males or of females.

2) Distribute supplies.

3) Give the following instructions to the groups:

> ➤ Using magazine pictures, phrases, and words, you are to make a collage that describes what your group sees as the qualities of men and women in today's society.

> ➤ Divide the sheet of paper in half.

> ➤ Use one half of the sheet of paper to illustrate the qualities of males and the other half to illustrate the qualities of females.

4) After the students complete their collages, have each group show and explain their collage.

5) Use the following questions for discussion:

✔ What are the major differences between the collages created by the males and females?

☞ *Many times, the boys create collages that show women as sex objects and men in macho roles. The females often create scenes of men and women in relationships, with women depicted in nurturing, caring roles.*

✔ Girls: How do you feel about the images that the boys used to depict you? Is their view of men and women realistic?

✔ Boys: How do you feel about the images that the girls used to depict you? Is their view of men and women realistic?

✔ Do you see any stereotyping in either set of collages?

✔ Did any of these works anger you? Surprise you? Upset you? Why?

TRAINER'S NOTES

©1994 Whole Person Press 210 W Michigan Duluth MN 55802   (800) 247-6789

VALUES

32 WHAT ARE THEY THINKING? (p 94)

This activity can be used to assess student values on many issues—particularly in the areas of chemical use and sexuality—by having students see whether their beliefs about the group's opinion is based on reality or just on what they think everyone else feels.
(Two short sessions)

33 I VALUE THIS (p 96)

Students have the opportunity to examine some of their primary values and then discover how these values fit into their views on sexual behavior. (1–2 hours)

34 THIS IS WHAT I VALUE (p 99)

Values are learned beliefs about what is right, good, true, and acceptable to the individual. This activity encourages students to clarify their values pertaining to various areas of wellness. (30–40 minutes)

32 WHAT ARE THEY THINKING?

This activity can be used to assess student values on many issues—particularly in the areas of chemical use and sexuality—by having students see whether their beliefs about the groups's opinion is based on reality or just on what they think everyone else feels.

GOAL

Compare true group values with what people think are the values and behaviors of the group.

TIME FRAME

Two short sessions: first session, 10 minutes; second session, 20–30 minutes

AGE GROUP

Upper Elementary to High School

MATERIALS NEEDED

Paper and pencils.

PROCESS

1) Distribute blank sheets of paper and tell the students that they are going to answer a confidential survey and are not to sign their names. On the top half of their paper have them answer questions similar to the following:

✔ What do you think others in this class think about smoking? (See note below.)

✔ Do they think it is OK? Not OK?

✔ How many people in this class do you think smoke?

☞ *Select topics that are appropriate for your class. You might ask questions about drinking, having sex, using drugs, cheating, eating disorders, etc.*

2) On the bottom half of the paper, have students answer the same questions as above, but this time focusing on themselves:

✔ What do you think about smoking?

✔ Is it OK? Not OK?

✔ Do you smoke?

☞ *Remind students that they can be as honest as they wish because their names will not be on their papers.*

3) Collect their papers and tabulate the results.

4) During the second session, share the results of the survey with the students and compare the projections of what they thought were the values and behaviors of the class to what the actual stated values and behaviors were.

5) Lead a discussion, using the following questions:

✔ Do you think most people were honest in their answers?

✔ Were the reported actual values and behaviors quite different from what you thought they were?

TRAINER'S NOTES

33 I VALUE THIS

Students have the opportunity to examine some of their primary values and then discover how these values fit into their views on sexual behavior.

GOALS

Assess students' strongest values.

Compare personal values to values supported by parents.

Analyze how personal values fit into sexual decision-making.

TIME FRAME

1–2 hours or 2 separate class periods

AGE GROUP

Junior and Senior High

MATERIALS NEEDED

Copies of the **I Value This** worksheet.

PROCESS

1) Begin with the following chalktalk:

- To live a life that is really by your own design, you need to clarify your personal values. Your values—the things you hold most dear—determine how you live and behave, what jobs you seek, and what friends you have. Values usually develop from what your parents, church, school, and community taught you. Values don't change from day to day. They are extremely important in our lives, and we make sacrifices to uphold them.

- For example, if your parents taught you that it was important to be kind to animals, you probably have that as a value in your life today and will probably go out of your way to help or care for a distressed or lost animal. However, if your parents taught you that animals are worthless, you will probably not respect them, and may even be cruel to them because you don't value them.

- Often, when we go against our values, we feel guilty. The reason many teens spend so much time feeling guilty is that they intentionally violate the values they were taught by their parents to see how important those values really are.

- The teen years are a critical time to test and choose personal values that will stay with you for the rest of your life.

- Some of these values, like those concerning your sexual behavior, result from the combination of many other values.

2) Distribute the **I Value This** worksheet.

3) Instruct students to rank the qualities on the sheet as to whether they are 1) very important, 2) important, or 3) not very important.

4) When the students are finished, tally their answers on the blackboard and note the top 3 values.

5) Have students go back to their worksheets and choose the top 3 values that they think their parents have.

6) Tally these answers, note the top 3 values, and then ask the following questions:

✔ Are there differences between your top values and your parents' top values?

✔ Overall how do the student values compare with the parental values?

7) Ask students to look at the relationship between their top 3 values and their personal values regarding sexual behavior. Do their major values carry over into their attitudes toward sexual behavior?

8) Have the students discuss how the class's top 3 values can be seen in regards to sexual behavior. Examples: Happiness—I want a relationship in my life that provides happiness for both partners. Love—caring and sharing is what makes love special, and in my relationships I want the love to be based on trust, respect, and mutual caring.

9) Now have students look at their own top 3 values and write statements that reflect their values as they specifically relate to sexual behavior.

I VALUE THIS

Looking at the following list, rank the importance of each value to yourself as very important, important, or unimportant, and then circle your top three values.

	Very important	Important	Unimportant
Respect			
Love			
Friends			
Money			
Grades			
Recognition			
Popularity			
Acceptance			
Caring			
Religion			
Excitement			
Honesty			
Bravery			
Appearance			
Health			
Academics			
Self-esteem			
Self-confidence			
Family			
Peace			

©1994 Whole Person Press 210 W Michigan Duluth MN 55802   (800) 247-6789

34   THIS IS WHAT I VALUE

Values are learned beliefs about what is right, good, true, and acceptable to the individual. This activity encourages students to clarify their values pertaining to various areas of wellness.

GOALS

To clarify the importance of wellness values in our lives.

To examine how values shape our preferences in life.

To examine how values are acted out through behavior.

TIME FRAME

30–40 minutes

AGE GROUP

Junior and Senior High

MATERIAL NEEDED

Copies of the **This Is What I Value** worksheet.

PROCESS

1) Begin the activity by handing out copies of the **This Is What I Value** worksheet and giving the following instructions:

   ➤ Your values show your preferences in life, and they are expressed through the ways you behave and the activities you participate in. Spend some time thinking about the values you have in your life.

   ➤ On the worksheet, identify as many of your values as you can pertaining to the areas of wellness specified. Next to each value, jot down a few thoughts on how you express your values in your everyday life.

2) After 15 minutes, lead a discussion on the values students found to be most important by asking the following questions:

   ✔ Why are these values so important to you?

   ✔ How did they get to be so important?

©1994 Whole Person Press 210 W Michigan Duluth MN 55802   (800) 247-6789

   ✔ What benefits do you find in holding these values dear to you?

   ✔ Do you ever get teased about your values? What do you do?

   ✔ Will these values last over your lifetime? Why or why not?

TRAINER'S NOTES

THIS IS WHAT I VALUE

Next to each of the wellness areas on the list below, write your personal value and an example of how you express this value in your life. For example: Spiritual   *Very important to me. I attend church each Sunday.*

Wellness area	My personal values	How I express these values
Nutrition		
Spiritual		
Physical		
Emotional		
Intellectual		
Stress		
Social		
Environmental		

Circle the two values you consider most important in your life. Why are these so important to you? _____
What do your values say about your life? _____
_____
Is there one area of wellness where there are more personal values than in other areas? _____
Is any area under-represented? _____

©1994 Whole Person Press 210 W Michigan Duluth MN 55802   (800) 247-6789

TRAINER'S NOTES

GENERAL WELLNESS CONCEPTS

35   HERE I AM (p 104)

This enjoyable activity enables students to introduce
themselves to others in a new, creative way.
(Enough time for everyone to share)

36   HEALTH AND WELLNESS TEAM (p 106)

This activity helps students take a look at current health
problems and examine ways in which a wellness lifestyle
can prevent or change some of these problems.
(45–60 minutes)

37   I'VE GOT THE PICTURE (p 108)

Students make up stories to review wellness principles.
(45 minutes)

38   CAREERS IN WELLNESS (p 110)

With the advent of the wellness movement, many
different careers have opened up. This activity encourages students to look at careers that relate to wellness.
(Extended period of time)

35 HERE I AM

This enjoyable activity enables students to introduce themselves to others in a new, creative way.

GOALS

Offers children an opportunity to share something about themselves in a nonthreatening way.

Helps students examine personal wellness concepts.

TIME FRAME

Enough time for everyone to share

☞ *If you have a large class, you may want to extend the activity over several days, using it as an introductory segment to each class, with several students sharing each day.*

AGE GROUP

Middle to Upper Elementary (adaptable to any age group)

MATERIALS NEEDED

None.

PROCESS

1) Ask students to describe something they are either wearing or carrying with them that represents an aspect of themselves.

   ☞ *Provide an example, such as, "I am wearing basketball shoes because I really like to play basketball," or "I have pink shoelaces because that is my favorite color."*

2) When everyone has finished, have a volunteer go around the group and try to repeat each student's name and his or her identifying possession.

VARIATION

■ Have students choose an object they are wearing, using, or carrying that represents an aspect of their health habits or wellness behavior.

Examples: "I am wearing braces so that my teeth can look their best."

"I am wearing running shoes because that is what I like to do for exercise." "I have carrots in my lunchbox because they are good for me and help me grow strong."

TRAINER'S NOTES

36 HEALTH AND WELLNESS TEAM

This activity helps students take a look at current health problems and examine ways in which a wellness lifestyle can prevent or change some of these problems.

GOALS

Examine current health problems.

Promote awareness of how positive lifestyle habits can help lessen or prevent many of these current health problems.

Help students integrate issues concerning health with those of wellness.

TIME FRAME

45–60 minutes

AGE GROUP

Junior and Senior High

MATERIALS NEEDED

None.

PROCESS

1) Copy the following chart on to the blackboard:

Health problems	Causes	Wellness lifestyles
Heart Disease	Smoking Sedentary life High cholesterol	Stop smoking Exercise Low fat diet
Suicide	Loneliness Depression	Develop friendships Seek counseling

2) Explain the chart to the students by saying the following:

- The left-hand column shows several major health problems and causes of death being faced today.

- The middle column shows some causes of these problems.

- The right-hand column shows the kinds of wellness lifestyles that can prevent or lessen these problems.

3) Have students add as many other examples of health problems, their causes, and wellness lifestyles to the chart they can think of.

VARIATION

■ After students have completed the chart, have them examine their own family history and report on any health problems that they might be susceptible to (i.e., hypertension, cancer, arthritis, osteoporosis, alcoholism, depression, etc.).

Have them decide upon a personal wellness goal that might help them prevent or lessen the chance of having this problem in their lives.

TRAINER'S NOTES

©1994 Whole Person Press 210 W Michigan Duluth MN 55802   (800) 247-6789

37 I'VE GOT THE PICTURE

Students make up stories to review wellness principles.

GOALS

Stimulate group creativity.

Review wellness principles.

TIME FRAME

45 minutes

AGE GROUP

Middle Elementary (adaptable for other age groups)

MATERIALS NEEDED

Magazine pictures of children and adults showing various expressions.

> ☞ *Cut out the pictures and mount them on cardboard prior to using this activity.*

PROCESS

1) Divide the class into groups of 4–5 people and distribute one picture to each group.

2) Assign each group a wellness topic, such as nutrition, exercise, feelings, stress, or self-esteem.

3) Give the following instructions:

   ➤ Your group is to create a story about the person in the picture you were given.

   ➤ The story must relate to the wellness topic your group was assigned.

   ➤ Each student must contribute at least one line to the story.

   ➤ Select a recorder to write your story.

4) When the students are finished, ask the members of each group to introduce the person in their picture and to tell that person's wellness story.

VARIATION

■ Assign the same topic to each group. Even though each group will be working on the same topic, their stories will vary because they received different pictures.

TRAINER'S NOTES

38 CAREERS IN WELLNESS

With the advent of the wellness movement, many different careers have opened up. This activity encourages students to look at careers that relate to wellness.

GOALS

Investigate careers that have to do with wellness.

Determine roles, responsibilities, and qualifications of individuals in these careers.

TIME FRAME

Extended period of time

AGE GROUP

Junior and Senior High

MATERIALS NEEDED

Copies of the **Wellness Careers** interview sheet.

PROCESS

1) Begin with a short chalktalk:

   - As society's attitudes about illness/health/wellness continue to grow and change, more jobs will be opening up in these areas. Many of these jobs will deal directly with the health of our communities.

   - It's a good idea for us to consider some of the jobs that may open up in the field of wellness to give us some ideas for possible future careers.

2) Have students interview representatives from health and wellness professions. You may want to invite these adult professionals to speak to the class or have students go out and interview them on-the-job.

3) Have students report back to the class about their findings concerning their particular career investigations.

WELLNESS CAREERS

Options for interviews: Health educator, exercise physiologist, nutritionist, cardiac rehab professional, government health analyst, fitness club operator, psychologist, holistic health practitioner, corporate wellness director, school wellness coordinator, community wellness director. Research your community for other wellness-related occupations.

Name _____ Career _____

1. How did you become interested in this career?

2. What kind of educational background is required by your profession?

3. What kind of job experience is necessary before entering your field?

4. How might your job change over the next twenty years?

5. Have your attitudes about health and wellness changed since you began your career?

6. What is the most rewarding thing about what you do?

7. What do you find most difficult in your career?

8. Do you expect the balance between professional care and self-care to change? Will this affect your profession?

9. How have society's attitudes about health changed since you began your career? Why do you think this is happening?

10. What advice would you give someone who is interested in your career field?

©1994 Whole Person Press 210 W Michigan Duluth MN 55802   (800) 247-6789

TRAINER'S NOTES

©1994 Whole Person Press 210 W Michigan Duluth MN 55802   (800) 247-6789

CLOSERS

39 COUNT TO TEN (p 114)

This is a lively activity that helps students participate as a group to review various areas of wellness. (20–30 minutes)

40 OPEN-ENDED CLOSINGS (p 116)

This simple process for eliciting feedback can be incorporated into the closing process for many activities and program segments. (5 minutes)

39 COUNT TO TEN

This is a lively activity that helps students participate as a group to review various areas of wellness.

GOALS

To help foster group thinking and cooperation.

To review various topics pertaining to wellness.

TIME FRAME

20–30 minutes

AGE GROUP

Adaptable for all

MATERIALS NEEDED

Two containers; ten pieces of paper numbered 1–10; ten 3" x 5" index cards with a different area of health and wellness written on each card: Nutrition, Fitness, Feelings, Relationships, Stress, Intellectual, Spiritual, Environmental, Self-esteem, Hygiene, etc.

PROCESS

1) Divide the class into either 5 or 10 groups. If you have 5 groups, each group can participate twice.

2) Put the numbered pieces of paper into one of the containers and the ten 3" x 5" cards into the other container.

3) Have one student from each group draw a number and another draw a wellness card.

4) The number tells the group how many different facts or suggestions about their topic the group must record. For example, if a group draws a "4" and "nutrition," group members must come up with 4 facts or suggestions about good nutrition to share with the whole class.

5) Give students several minutes for discussion. Appoint one recorder for each group.

6) When the groups are finished, have the recorders present their group's facts and suggestions to the rest of the class.

VARIATION

■ You may want to have a number spinner instead of number pieces. The group can then spin for their numbers.

> ☞ *This is an excellent activity for review of any wellness area. You can use the activity solely for nutrition, fitness, or whatever you prefer. The cards would then list topics within the subject matter that you want to preview or review (i.e., for nutrition, the cards could say "vitamins," "protein," " fats," etc.).*

TRAINER'S NOTES

40 OPEN-ENDED CLOSINGS

This simple process for eliciting feedback can be incorporated into the closing process for many activities and program segments.

GOALS

To provide students with ways to give feedback about activities.

To provide facilitators with a method for checking on how students feel about themselves, the activities, and the program.

To help bring closure to activities and program segments.

TIME FRAME

Five minutes at the end of each activity, class, or program segment

AGE GROUP

Adaptable for all

MATERIALS NEEDED

Blackboard.

PROCESS

1) On the following page, you'll find a list of open-ended statements that can be used for this activity. Choose several that apply to your particular activity or program segment, or make up your own, and write them on the blackboard or reproduce them for each student.

2) Tell students to answer the open-ended statements and then to hand in their papers to you, unsigned, on the way out of class.

3) You can share results with the class at the next meeting, or you can use them as a barometer of how your activities are progressing.

   ☞ *Open-ended responses are wonderful, but like anything else, they can be overused. Used judiciously, they can be an excellent way to keep tabs on how your students feel about what is going on in your class.*

If I want to be well, I will have to . . . To feel better, I need to . . . To have better friends, I need to . . . To feel better about myself, I need to . . . To get along with my parents better, I need to . . . To handle peer pressure better, I need to . . . To be more physically well, I need to . . . To have better nutritional wellness, I need to . . . To have a better sense of purpose for my life, I need to . . . To handle stress better, I need to . . .

My biggest worry is . . . My biggest family risk factor is . . . My biggest personal risk factor is . . . It doesn't matter to me that I . . . I am most proud of . . . I don't care about . . . I need to do something about . . . I don't see any need to . . . What scares me most about life is . . . What excites me most about life is . . . Wellness classes are . . .

Stress is . . . Love is . . . Health is . . . Illness is . . . Friends are . . . Parents are . . . Most teachers are . . . Some friends are . . . Best friends are . . . My friends are . . . My friends see me as . . . I see myself as . . . The thing I like most about myself is . . . The thing I like least about myself is . . .

I look forward to . . . I dread . . . Other people usually . . . You are really successful when . . . When people think of me they usually . . . When I was a child . . . I want to be . . . Drugs are . . . Smoking is . . . I really want . . . The best teacher in the world . . . My dream is to . . . My body is . . . Sex is . . . This group is . . . This class is . . . I need . . . My parents don't know that I . . .

Health professionals can't . . . Nutrition is . . . Fitness is . . . Sexual responsibility is . . . If I could change one thing in the environment it would be . . . The most important thing in my life is . . . The part of my body where I collect tension is . . .

My wish for the world is . . . My wish for my family is . . . My wish for myself is . . . I learned that I . . . I realized that I . . . I relearned that I . . . I was surprised that . . . I noticed that I . . . I was pleased that I . . . I discovered that the class . . . I was displeased that . . .

I need to be loved because . . . I am loved by . . . I belong to . . . I like myself when . . . I don't like myself when . . . I like other people when . . . I don't like other people when . . . The person who means the most to me is . . .

I hope . . . I wish . . . I fear . . . I want . . . I am afraid of . . . I envy . . .

In today's class I wish . . . In today's class I am sorry I . . . Today's class would have meant more if . . . I think it is unfair that . . . What I really like about wellness classes is . . .

Five years from now . . . Ten years from now . . . Teenagers are . . . Most of us feel . . . The best way to feel good about yourself is . . .

©1994 Whole Person Press 210 W Michigan Duluth MN 55802   (800) 247-6789

TRAINER'S NOTES

RESOURCES

WORKSHOP NOTES

Date:

Place:

Name of Workshop:

Exercises Used:

Description of the Group:

Observations / Comments / Things to Remember for Next Time:

©1994 Whole Person Press 210 W Michigan Duluth MN 55802   (800) 247-6789

TRAINER'S NOTES

WORKSHOP NOTES

Date:

Place:

Name of Workshop:

Exercises Used:

Description of the Group:

Observations / Comments / Things to Remember for Next Time:

©1994 Whole Person Press 210 W Michigan Duluth MN 55802   (800) 247-6789

TRAINER'S NOTES

WORKSHOP NOTES

Date:

Place:

Name of Workshop:

Exercises Used:

Description of the Group:

Observations / Comments / Things to Remember for Next Time:

©1994 Whole Person Press 210 W Michigan Duluth MN 55802   (800) 247-6789

TRAINER'S NOTES

WORKSHOP NOTES

Date:

Place:

Name of Workshop:

Exercises Used:

Description of the Group:

Observations / Comments / Things to Remember for Next Time:

TRAINER'S NOTES

WORKSHOP NOTES

Date:

Place:

Name of Workshop:

Exercises Used:

Description of the Group:

Observations / Comments / Things to Remember for Next Time:

TRAINER'S NOTES

WORKSHOP NOTES

Date:

Place:

Name of Workshop:

Exercises Used:

Description of the Group:

Observations / Comments / Things to Remember for Next Time:

TRAINER'S NOTES

WORKSHOP NOTES

Date:

Place:

Name of Workshop:

Exercises Used:

Description of the Group:

Observations / Comments / Things to Remember for Next Time:

TRAINER'S NOTES

WHOLE PERSON ASSOCIATES RESOURCES

Our materials are designed to address the whole person—physical, emotional, mental, spiritual, and social. Developed for trainers by trainers, all of these resources are ready-to-use. Novice trainers will find everything they need to get started, and the expert trainer will discover new ideas and concepts to add to their existing programs.

GROUP PROCESS RESOURCES

All of the exercises in our group process resources encourage interaction between the leader and participants, as well as among the participants. Each exercise includes everything you need to present a meaningful program: goals, optimal group size, time frame, materials list, and the complete process instructions.

WELLNESS ACTIVITIES FOR YOUTH
Volume 2

Sandy Queen

The second volume of **Wellness Activities for Youth** continues to help leaders teach children and teenagers about wellness with a whole person approach, a "no put-down" rule, and most of all, an emphasis on FUN. The concepts include:

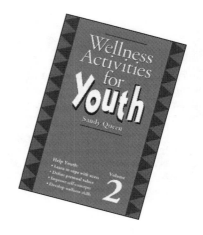

- values
- spiritual wellness
- thinking skills
- emotional health
- substance abuse

WELLNESS ACTIVITIES FOR YOUTH
WORKSHEET MASTERS

Complete packages of full-size (8 1/2" x 11") photocopy masters that include all the worksheets and handouts from **Wellness Activities for Youth Volumes 1 and 2** are available to you. Use the masters for easy duplication of the handouts for each participant.

- ❑ **WY1 / Wellness Activities for Youth Volume 1 / $19.95**
- ❑ **WY2 / Wellness Activities for Youth Volume 2 / $19.95**
- ❑ **WY1W / Wellness Activities for Youth V. 1 Worksheet Masters / $9.95**
- ❑ **WY2W / Wellness Activities for Youth V. 2 Worksheet Masters / $9.95**

©1994 Whole Person Press 210 W Michigan Duluth MN 55802   (800) 247-6789

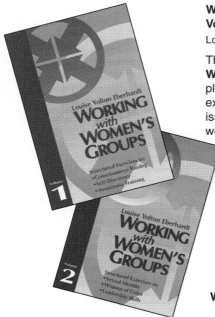

WORKING WITH WOMEN'S GROUPS
Volumes 1 & 2
Louise Yolton Eberhardt

The two volumes of **Working with Women's Groups** have been completely revised and updated. These exercises will help women explore issues that are of perennial concern as well as today's hot topics.

Volume 1:
- consciousness-raising
- self-discovery
- assertiveness training

Volume 2:
- sexuality issues
- women of color
- leadership skills training

WORKING WITH WOMEN'S GROUPS WORKSHEET MASTERS

Complete packages of full-size (8 1/2" x 11") photocopy masters that include all the worksheets and handouts from **Working with Women's Groups volume 1 and 2** are available to you. Use the masters for easy duplication of the handouts for each participant.

- ❏ **WG1 / Working with Women's Groups—Volume 1 / $24.95**
- ❏ **WG2 / Working with Women's Groups—Volume 2 / $24.95**
- ❏ **WG1W / Working with Women's Groups—Volume 1 Worksheet Masters / $9.95**
- ❏ **WG2W / Working with Women's Groups—Volume 2 Worksheet Masters / $9.95**

WORKING WITH MEN'S GROUPS
Roger Karsk and Bill Thomas

Also revised and updated, this volume is a valuable resource for anyone working with men's groups. The exercises cover a variety of topics, including:

- self discovery
- parenting
- conflict
- intimacy

- ❏ **MG / Working with Men's Groups / $24.95**
- ❏ **MGW / Working with Men's Groups Worksheet Masters / $9.95**

©1994 Whole Person Press 210 W Michigan Duluth MN 55802   (800) 247-6789

WORKING WITH GROUPS FROM DYSFUNCTIONAL FAMILIES

Cheryl Hetherington

This collection of 29 proven group activities is designed to heal the pain that results from growing up in or living in a dysfunctional family. With these exercises you can:

- promote healing
- build self-esteem
- encourage sharing
- help participants acknowledge their feelings

WORKING WITH GROUPS FROM DYSFUNCTIONAL FAMILIES REPRODUCIBLE WORKSHEET MASTERS

A complete package of full-size (8 1/2" x 11") photocopy masters that include all the worksheets and handouts from **Working with Groups from Dysfunctional Families** is available to you. Use the masters for easy duplication of the handouts for each participant.

❑ **DFH / Working with Groups from Dysfunctional Families / $24.95**
❑ **DFW / Dysfunctional Families Worksheet Masters / $9.95**

PLAYFUL ACTIVITIES FOR POWERFUL PRESENTATIONS

Bruce Williamson

This book contains 40 fun exercises designed to fit any group or topic. These exercises will help you:

- build teamwork
- encourage laughter and playfulness
- relieve stress and tension
- free up the imaginations of participants

❑ **PAP / Playful Activities for Powerful Presentations $19.95**

©1994 Whole Person Press 210 W Michigan Duluth MN 55802   (800) 247-6789

STRUCTURED EXERCISES
IN STRESS MANAGEMENT—VOLUMES 1-4
Nancy Loving Tubesing, EdD and Donald A. Tubesing, PhD, Editors

Each book in this four-volume series contains 36 ready-to-use teaching modules that involve the participant—as a whole person—in learning how to manage stress more effectively.

Each exercise is carefully designed by top stress-management professionals. Instructions are clearly written and field-tested so that even beginning trainers can smoothly lead a group through warm-up and closure, reflection and planning, and action and interaction—all with minimum preparation time.

Each Stress Handbook is brimming with practical ideas that you can weave into your own teaching designs or mix and match to develop new programs for varied settings, audiences, and time frames. In each volume you'll find **Icebreakers, Stress Assessments, Management Strategies, Skill Builders, Action Planners, Closing Processes** and **Group Energizers**—all with a special focus on stress management.

STRUCTURED EXERCISES
IN WELLNESS PROMOTION—VOLUMES 1-4
Nancy Loving Tubesing, EdD and Donald A. Tubesing, PhD, Editors

Discover the Wellness Handbooks—from the wellness pioneers at Whole Person Associates. Each volume in this innovative series includes 36 experiential learning activities that focus on whole person health—body, mind, spirit, emotions, relationships, and lifestyle.

The exercises, developed by an interdisciplinary pool of leaders in the wellness movement nationwide, actively encourage people to adopt wellness-oriented attitudes and to develop more responsible self-care patterns.

All process designs in the Wellness Handbooks are clearly explained and have been thoroughly field-tested with diverse audiences so that trainers can use them with confidence. **Icebreakers, Wellness Explorations, Self-Care Strategies, Action Planners, Closings** and **Group Energizers** are all ready-to-go—including reproducible worksheets, scripts, and chalktalk outlines—for the busy professional who wants to develop unique wellness programs without spending oodles of time in preparation.

©1994 Whole Person Press 210 W Michigan Duluth MN 55802   (800) 247-6789

STRUCTURED EXERCISES IN STRESS AND WELLNESS ARE AVAILABLE IN TWO FORMATS

LOOSE-LEAF FORMAT (8 1/2" x 11")

The loose-leaf, 3-ring binder format provides you with maximum flexiblity. The binder gives you plenty of room to add your own adaptations, workshop outlines, or notes right where you need them. The index tabs offer quick and easy access to each section of exercises, and the generous margins allow plenty of room for notes. In addition an extra set of the full-size worksheets and handouts are packaged separately for convenient duplication.

SOFTCOVER FORMAT (6" x 9")

The softcover format is a perfect companion to the loose-leaf version. This smaller book fits easily into your briefcase or bag, and the binding has been designed to remain open on your desk or lecturn. Worksheets and handouts can be enlarged and photocopied for distribution to your participants, or you can purchase sets of worksheet masters.

WORKSHEET MASTERS

The Worksheet Masters for the two Structured Exercise series offer full-size (8 1/2" x 11") photocopy masters. All of the worksheets and handouts for each volume are reproduced in easy-to-read print with professional graphics. All you need to do to complete your workshop preparation is run them through a copier.

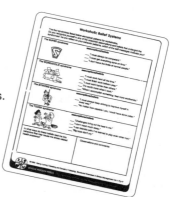

Structured Exercises in Stress Management

- ❏ **Loose-Leaf Edition—Volume 1-4 / $54.95 each**
- ❏ **Softcover Edition—Volume 1-4 / $29.95 each**
- ❏ **Worksheet Masters—Volume 1-4 / $9.95 each**

Structured Exercises in Wellness Promotion

- ❏ **Loose-Leaf Edition—Volume 1-4 / $54.95 each**
- ❏ **Softcover Edition—Volume 1-4 / $29.95 each**
- ❏ **Worksheet Masters—Volume 1-4 / $9.95 each**

©1994 Whole Person Press 210 W Michigan Duluth MN 55802   (800) 247-6789

WORKSHOPS-IN-A-BOOK

KICKING YOUR STRESS HABITS:
A Do-it-yourself Guide to Coping with Stress
Donald A. Tubesing, PhD

Over a quarter of a million people have found ways to deal with their everyday stress by using **Kicking Your Stress Habits**. This workshop-in-a-book actively involves the reader in assessing stressful patterns and developing more effective coping strategies with helpful "Stop and Reflect" sections in each chapter.

The 10-step planning process and 20 skills for managing stress make **Kicking Your Stress Habits** an ideal text for stress management classes in many different settings, from hospitals to universities and for a wide variety of groups.

❑ **K / Kicking Your Stress Habits / 14.95**

SEEKING YOUR HEALTHY BALANCE:
A Do-it-yourself Guide to Whole Person Well-being
Donald A. Tubesing, PhD and Nancy Loving Tubesing, EdD

Where can you find the time and energy to "do it all" without sacrificing your health and well-being? **Seeking Your Healthy Balance** helps the reader discover how to make changes toward a more balanced lifestyle by learning effective ways to juggle work, self, and others; clarifying self-care options; and discovering and setting their own personal priorities.

Seeking Your Healthy Balance asks the questions and helps readers find their own answers.

❑ **HB / Seeking Your Healthy Balance / 14.95**

©1994 Whole Person Press 210 W Michigan Duluth MN 55802   (800) 247-6789

RELAXATION RESOURCES

Many trainers and workshop leaders have discovered the benefits of relaxation and visualization in healing the body, mind, and spirit.

30 SCRIPTS FOR RELAXATION, IMAGERY, AND INNER HEALING
Julie Lusk

These two volumes are collections of relaxation scripts created by trainers for trainers. The 30 scripts in each of the two volumes have been professionally-tested and fine-tuned so they are ready to use for both novice and expert trainers.

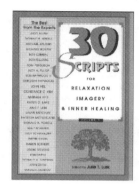

Help your participants change their behavior, enhance their self-esteem, discover inner, private places, and heal themselves through simple trainer-led guided imagery scripts. Both volumes include information on how to use the scripts, suggestions for tailoring them to your specific needs and audience, and information on how to successfully incorporate guided imagery into your existing programs.

❑ 30S / 30 Scripts for Relaxation, Imagery, and Inner Healing—Volume 1 / $19.95
❑ 30S2 / 30 Scripts for Relaxation, Imagery, and Inner Healing—Volume 2 / $19.95

INQUIRE WITHIN
Andrew Schwartz

Use visualization to make positive changes in your life. The 24 visualization experiences in **Inquire Within** will help participants enhance their creativity, heal inner pain, learn to relax, and deal with conflict. Each visualization includes questions at the end of the process that encourage deeper reflection and a better understanding of the exercise and the response it invokes.

❑ IW / Inquire Within / $19.95

RELAXATION AUDIOTAPES

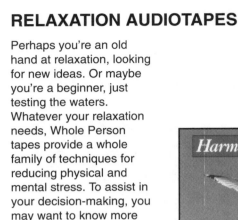

Perhaps you're an old hand at relaxation, looking for new ideas. Or maybe you're a beginner, just testing the waters. Whatever your relaxation needs, Whole Person tapes provide a whole family of techniques for reducing physical and mental stress. To assist in your decision-making, you may want to know more about different types of relaxation.

We offer six different types of relaxation techniques in our twenty-one tapes. The Whole Person series ranges from simple breathing and stretching exercises, to classic autogenic and progressive relaxation sequences, to guided meditations and whimsical daydreams. All are carefully crafted to promote whole person relaxation—body, mind, and spirit. We also provide a line of music-only tapes, composed specifically for relaxation.

SENSATIONAL RELAXATION

When stress piles up, it becomes a heavy load both physically and emotionally. These full-length relaxation experiences will teach you techniques that can be used whenever you feel that stress is getting out of control. Choose one you like and repeat it daily until it becomes second nature then recall that technique whenever you need it.

- ❑ **CD / Countdown to Relaxation / $9.95**
- ❑ **DS / Daybreak / Sundown / $9.95**
- ❑ **TDB / Take a Deep Breath / $9.95**
- ❑ **RLX / Relax . . . Let Go . . . Relax / $9.95**
- ❑ **SRL / StressRelease / $9.95**
- ❑ **WRM / Warm and Heavy / $9.95**

STRESS BREAKS

Do you need a short energy booster or a quick stress reliever? If you don't know what type of relaxation you like, or if you are new to guided relaxation techniques, try one of our Stress Breaks for a quick refocusing or change of pace any time of the day.

- ❑ **BT / BreakTime / $9.95**
- ❑ **NT / Natural Tranquilizers / $9.95**

DAYDREAMS

Escape from the stress around you with guided tours to beautiful places. Picture yourself traveling to the ocean, sitting in a park, luxuriating in the view from the majestic mountains, or enjoying the solitude and serenity of a cozy cabin. The 10-minute escapes included in our Daydream tapes will lead your imagination away from your everyday cares so you can resume your tasks relaxed and comforted.

- ❑ **DD1 / Daydreams 1: Getaways / $9.95**
- ❑ **DD2 / Daydreams 2: Peaceful Places / $9.95**

GUIDED MEDITATION

Take a step beyond relaxation and discover the connection between body and mind with guided meditation. The imagery in our full-length meditations will help you discover your strengths, find healing, make positive life changes, and recognize your inner wisdom.

- ❑ **IH / Inner Healing / $9.95**
- ❑ **PE / Personal Empowering / $9.95**
- ❑ **HBT / Healthy Balancing / $9.95**
- ❑ **SPC / Spiritual Centering / $9.95**

WILDERNESS DAYDREAMS

Discover the healing power of nature with the four tapes in the Wilderness Daydreams series. The eight special journeys will transport you from your harried, stressful surroundings to the peaceful serenity of words and water.

- ❑ **WD1 / Canoe / Rain / $9.95**
- ❑ **WD2 / Island /Spring / $9.95**
- ❑ **WD3 / Campfire / Stream / $9.95**
- ❑ **WD4 / Sailboat / Pond / $9.95**

MUSIC ONLY

No relaxation program would be complete without relaxing melodies that can be played as background to a prepared script or that can be enjoyed as you practice a technique you have already learned. Steven Eckels composed his melodies specifically for relaxation. These "musical prayers for healing" will calm your body, mind, and spirit.

- ❑ **T / Tranquility / $9.95**
- ❑ **H / Harmony / $9.95**
- ❑ **S / Serenity / $9.95**

Titles can be combined for discounts!

QUANTITY DISCOUNT			
1 - 9	10 - 49	50 - 99	100+
$9.95	$8.95	$7.96	CALL

©1994 Whole Person Press 210 W Michigan Duluth MN 55802   (800) 247-6789

ORDER FORM

Name _____

Address _____

City _____

State/Zip _____

Area Code/Telephone _____

Please make checks payable to:
Whole Person Associates Inc
210 West Michigan
Duluth MN 55802-1908
FAX: 1-218-727-0505
TOLL FREE: 1-800-247-6789

Books / Workshops-In-A-Book
___ Kicking Your Stress Habits .... $14.95 _____
___ Seeking Your Healthy Balance .... $14.95 _____

Structured Exercises in Stress Management Series—Volumes 1-4
___ Stress Softcover Edition .... Vol 1 ___ Vol 2 ___ Vol 3 ___ Vol 4 ___ $29.95 _____
___ Stress Loose-Leaf Edition .... Vol 1 ___ Vol 2 ___ Vol 3 ___ Vol 4 ___ $54.95 _____
___ Stress Worksheet Masters .... Vol 1 ___ Vol 2 ___ Vol 3 ___ Vol 4 ___ $9.95 _____

Structured Exercises in Wellness Promotion Series—Volumes 1-4
___ Wellness Softcover Edition .... Vol 1 ___ Vol 2 ___ Vol 3 ___ Vol 4 ___ $29.95 _____
___ Wellness Loose-Leaf Edition .... Vol 1 ___ Vol 2 ___ Vol 3 ___ Vol 4 ___ $54.95 _____
___ Wellness Worksheet Masters .... Vol 1 ___ Vol 2 ___ Vol 3 ___ Vol 4 ___ $9.95 _____

Group Process Resources
___ Playful Activities for Powerful Presentations .... $19.95 _____
___ Working with Groups from Dysfunctional Families .... $24.95 _____
___ Working with Groups from Dysfunctional Families Worksheet Masters .... $9.95 _____
___ Working with Women's Groups .... Vol 1 ___ Vol 2 ___ $24.95 _____
___ Working with Women's Groups Worksheet Masters .... Vol 1 ___ Vol 2 ___ $9.95 _____
___ Working with Men's Groups .... $24.95 _____
___ Working with Men's Groups Worksheet Masters .... $9.95 _____
___ Wellness Activities for Youth .... Vol 1 ___ Vol 2 ___ $19.95 _____
___ Wellness Activities for Youth Worksheet Masters .... Vol 1 ___ Vol 2 ___ $9.95 _____

Relaxation Audiotapes
___ BreakTime .... $ 9.95 _____
___ Countdown to Relaxation .... $ 9.95 _____
___ Daybreak/Sundown .... $ 9.95 _____
___ Daydreams 1: Getaways .... $ 9.95 _____
___ Daydreams 2: Peaceful Places .... $ 9.95 _____
___ Harmony (music only) .... $ 9.95 _____
___ Healthy Balancing .... $ 9.95 _____
___ Inner Healing .... $ 9.95 _____
___ Natural Tranquilizers .... $ 9.95 _____
___ Personal Empowering .... $ 9.95 _____
___ Relax . . . Let Go . . . Relax .... $ 9.95 _____
___ Serenity (music only) .... $ 9.95 _____
___ Spiritual Centering .... $ 9.95 _____
___ StressRelease .... $ 9.95 _____
___ Take a Deep Breath .... $ 9.95 _____
___ Tranquility (music only) .... $ 9.95 _____
___ Warm and Heavy .... $ 9.95 _____
___ Wilderness DD 1: Canoe/Rain .... $ 9.95 _____
___ Wilderness DD 2: Island/Spring .... $ 9.95 _____
___ Wilderness DD 3: Campfire/Stream .... $ 9.95 _____
___ Wilderness DD 4: Sailboat/Pond .... $ 9.95 _____

Relaxation Resources
___ 30 Scripts—Volume 1 .... $19.95 _____
___ 30 Scripts—Volume 2 .... $19.95 _____
___ Inquire Within .... $19.95 _____

My check is enclosed. **(US funds only)**

Please charge my_____Visa _____Mastercard

_____

Exp date _____

Signature _____

SUBTOTAL _____
TAX (MN residents 6.5%) _____
7% GST-Canadian customers only _____
**SHIPPING _____
GRAND TOTAL _____

800-247-6789

** **SHIPPING.** $5.00 ($8.00 outside U.S.)
Please call us for quotes on UPS 3rd Day,
2nd Day or Next Day Air.

About Whole Person Associates

At Whole Person Associates, we're 100% committed to providing stress and wellness materials that involve participants and have a "whole person" focus—body, mind, spirit, and relationships.

That's our mission and it's very important to us—but it doesn't tell the whole story. Behind the products in our catalog is a company full of people—and *that's* what really makes us who we are.

ABOUT THE OWNERS

Whole Person Associates was created by the vision of two people: Donald A. Tubesing, PhD, and Nancy Loving Tubesing, EdD. Since way back in 1970, Don and Nancy have been active in the stress management/wellness promotion movement—consulting, leading seminars, writing, and publishing. Most of our early products were the result of their creativity and expertise.

Living proof that you can "stay evergreen," Don and Nancy remain the driving force behind the company and are still very active in developing new products that touch people's lives.

ABOUT THE COMPANY

Whole Person Associates was "born" in Duluth, Minnesota, and we remain committed to our lovely city on the shore of Lake Superior. All of our operations are here, which makes communication between departments much easier! We've grown since our beginnings, but at a steady pace—we're interested in sustainable growth that allows us to keep our down-to-earth orientation.

We put the same high quality into every product we offer, translating the best of current research into practical, accessible, easy-to-use materials. In this way we can create the best possible resources to help our customers teach about stress management and wellness promotion.

We also strive to treat our customers as we would like to be treated. If we fall short of our goals in any way, please let us know.

ABOUT OUR EMPLOYEES

Speaking of down-to-earth, that's a requirement for each and every one of our employees. We're all product consultants, which means that anyone who answers the phone can probably answer your questions (if they can't, they'll find someone who can.)

We focus on helping you find the products that fit your needs. And we've found that the best way to do that is to hire friendly and resourceful people.

ABOUT OUR ASSOCIATES

Who are the "associates" in Whole Person Associates? They're the trainers, authors, musicians, and others who have developed much of the material you see on these pages. We're always on the lookout for high-quality products that reflect our "whole person" philosophy and fill a need for our customers.

Most of our products were developed by experts who are the tops in their fields, and we're very proud to be associated with them.

ABOUT OUR CUSTOMERS

Finally, we wouldn't have a reason to exist without you, our customers. We've met some of you, and we've talked to many more of you on the phone. We are always aware that without you, there would be no Whole Person Associates.

That's why we'd love to hear from you! Let us know what you think of our products—how you use them in your work, what additional products you'd like to see, and what shortcomings you've noted. Write us or call on our toll-free line. We look forward to hearing from you!